Nelson practice book of **PHRASAL VERBS**

REVISED EDITION

Nelson

Thomas Nelson and Sons Ltd
Nelson House   Mayfield Road
Walton-on-Thames   Surrey KT12 5PL

51 York Place
Edinburgh   EH1 3JD

Thomas Nelson (Hong Kong) Ltd
Toppan Building 10/F
22A Westlands Road
Quarry Bay   Hong Kong

ISBN 0-17-555868-X
NPN 13 12 11 10 9 8 7 6

Printed in Hong Kong

Classification

All the verbs are classified to show how they are used with objects and pronouns:

With object nouns or noun phrases:

N1 take **your hat** off; put **prices** up.
N2 look for **the keys**; call on **your friends**.

With object pronouns:

P1 take **it** off; read **them** out.
P2 look for **them**; get in touch with **me**.

Without direct objects:

Intransitive, no direct object:
Ø I fell over; they turned up.

Followed by the gerund:

G give up **smoking**; carry on **watching** television.

For example:

put out is N1 N2 P1	put a fire out; put out a fire; put it out.
look round is N2 P2 Ø	look round a shop; look round it; look round.
go on is Ø G	go on; go on doing something.
look forward to is N2 P2 G	look forward to your holiday; look forward to it; look forward to going on holiday.
turn out is Ø	turn out all right; turn out to be all right.

The classification is repeated at the bottom of every page, for ease of reference.

In the aeroplane James's mother gave the boarding cards to the stewardess, who **showed** them **to** their seats. They sat down, and his mother showed him how to **do up** his seat belt.

'Sit still, and don't **get up** until I say you can,' she said, lighting a cigarette.

'No smoking until we are in the air, please,' said a stewardess.

'I'm sorry,' answered James's mother. 'I'll **put** it **out**.'

'Are we going to **take off** now, Mum?' asked James, eager to be in the sky. 'My favourite bit is when the plane **speeds up** and pushes you back into your seat.'

Notes

show to	N1 P1	A stewardess shows you to your seat.
do up	N1 N2 P1	You do your belt or your clothes up.
get up	Ø	You get up at the end of a lesson, a film or a meal.
put out	N1 N2 P1	You put out a cigarette, a light or a fire.
take off	Ø	A plane or rocket takes off.
speed up	N1 N2 P1 Ø	A plane, a car or a person speeds up when it starts to move faster. You can also speed up a motor.

Exercise A

Complete these sentences:

1 Your shoelace is undone. . . . it . . . before you have an accident.
2 The aeroplane . . . . . . on time in spite of the fog.
3 Please don't . . . . Remain in your seat.
4 The waiter took his coat and . . . him . . . a table.
5 . . . . . . that cigarette. This is a non-smoking compartment.
6 I could feel the car . . . . . . as I pressed the accelerator.
7 Some of the lights are still on. Could you . . . them . . . when you leave?
8 He forgot to . . . . his shirt before entering the church.

Exercise B

Answer these questions:

1 What do you do with a cigarette when it is finished?
2 What do you do with shoelaces?
3 What do you do to the lights before going to bed?
4 What takes off?
5 When do you get up?
6 Can you do up a tie?
7 When does a car speed up?
8 What does an usherette in a cinema do?

N1	Take *your hat* off	N2	Look for *the keys*	P1	Take *it* off
P2	Look for *them*	Ø	I fell over	G	Give up *smoking*

Jane:	You're not properly awake yet, are you?
Sarah:	How do you know?
Jane:	Well, look how you've **made up** your face. And you shirt is **done up** so that one side is higher than the other.
Sarah:	Oh dear. I look awful.
Jane:	I'd have a wash and start again, if I were you.
Sarah:	It's terrible. I **keep on** oversleeping. I **wake up** late nearly every day, and I have to **get up** in a hurry . . .
Jane:	I know just what it's like. I never get enough time to myself in the mornings.
Sarah:	Time! I don't have time to **see to** the children's breakfast, let alone worry about anything else.

Notes

make up	N1 N2 P1 Ø	You make your face up with cosmetics or make-up. You can also make (yourself) up.
keep on	G	When you keep on talking you talk repeatedly.
wake up	N1 N2 P1 Ø	An alarm clock wakes you up. When you hear it you wake up.
get up	N1 P1 Ø	You get up in the morning. You get a baby up.
see to	N2 P2	When a job needs to be done you see to it.
do up	N1 N2 P1	*See Unit 1*

Exercise A

Complete these sentences:

1 You'd better . . . your buttons . . .; there's a cold wind today.
2 I think he's still asleep. I'll go and . . . him . . ..
3 In the pantomime, Jan was . . . . . . to look like a Chinese princess.
4 I'm off to bed now, as I have to . . . . . . early tomorrow.
5 He was a very heavy sleeper and didn't . . . . . . when his alarm rang.
6 Her doctor told her not to smoke but she . . . . . . doing it.
7 A dairy farmer has to . . . . . . his cows every morning.
8 She had . . . her eyes . . . to look larger than they were.

Exercise B

Answer these questions:

1 What time do you wake up?
2 Name four things you can do up.
3 What do you do when you see to a meal?
4 Will you keep on studying English until you speak it perfectly?
5 Do you get up immediately after you wake up?
6 What does an actor do before going on stage?
7 Does your teacher keep on asking you questions?
8 Who sees to staff problems in a company?

N1	Take *your hat* off	N2	Look for *the keys*	P1	Take *it* off
P2	Look for *them*	Ø	I fell over	G	Give up *smoking*

'George, could you do me a favour?'

'Yes, sure.'

'**Show** Mr Frascatti **to** the conference room, would you? The meeting's due to start soon.'

'No. Haven't you heard? **It's off**; the manager's cancelled it because he wants to **sort out** the new advertising displays himself.'

'What? They've cancelled a major meeting, just because the boss wants to **see to** the advertising for a change? I don't know what to **make of** this company. Well, I'd better go and explain things to Mr Frascatti. But goodness knows what he will **think of** this.'

Notes

be off	Ø	If you cancel something which has been arranged you say it is off e.g. 'Saturday's match is off – there's been too much rain.'
sort out	N1 N2 P1	If you arrange things in order, or organise them in some way you sort them out.
make of	N2 P2	This is usually used in interrogative or negative sentences e.g. 'What do you make of this? I can't make anything of it at all.'
think of	N2 P2	If Mr Frascatti were not impressed he would say 'I don't think much of how you handle things here,' or 'I don't think much of it.'
show to	N1 P1	*See Unit 1*
see to	N2 P2	*See Unit 2*

Exercise A

Complete these sentences:

1 When they arrived at the prison, the men were . . . . . . into their various trades.
2 Can you . . . . . . the post as soon as possible?
3 I didn't . . . much . . . that film.
4 There was a mistake: nobody told him the trip . . . .
5 It was difficult to . . . anything . . . his handwriting.
6 The visiting lecturer was . . . . . . the lecture hall.
7 The match . . . . . . because there has been an outbreak of 'flu in the school.
8 He began to unpack his clothes and . . . them . . ..

Exercise B

Answer these questions:

1 What do you think of modern art?
2 When would you show someone to the door?
3 How does a librarian sort out books?
4 What would you do if you heard that a play you had tickets for was off?
5 What do you make of English grammar?
6 Who sees to the maintenance of a swimming-pool?
7 What do you think of your English?
8 How would you sort out a pack of cards?

N1 Take *your hat* off	N2 Look for *the keys*	P1 Take *it* off
P2 Look for *them*	Ø I fell over	G Give up *smoking*

3

UNIT 4 — *A Problem at the Airport*

When they arrived at the airport, they went straight to the desk, **checked in** and collected their boarding cards. Then, as they were buying a cup of coffee, the public address system **called out** Nigel's name.

'I wonder what they want,' he said. 'Can you **look after** the bags, Jill? I hope they get it **sorted out** before the plane **takes off**.'

He heard his name being called again.

'**Hold on**,' he said. 'I'm coming.'

Notes

check in   Ø   At the airport you go to the check-in desk to say you have arrived. You check in.

call out   N1 N2 P1   A public address system or a person calls out messages or announcements.

look after   N2 P2   A babysitter looks after children.

sort out   N1 N2 P1   You sort out a problem which has to be solved.

hold on   Ø   This is usually used in conversation, when you want someone to wait e.g. 'Tell him to hold on, I'm on my way.'

take off   Ø   *See Unit 1*

Exercise A

Complete these sentences:

1 We'll have to . . . . . . this problem before it gets worse.
2 The receptionist asked if he would . . . . . . as the manager was busy.
3 Ramon will . . . . . . the dogs while we are on holiday.
4 It is a difficult situation, and that is why you must . . . it . . . quickly.
5 The rocket . . . . . . from the NASA base in Houston.
6 Before he died, her father made her promise to . . . . . . her young brother.
7 He nearly missed the plane because he forgot to . . . .
8 When the nurse . . . . . . his name, he went into the surgery.

Exercise B

Answer these questions:

1 What does a marriage counsellor do?
2 What can you see from the control tower in an airport?
3 What is a public address system for?
4 What must you do before taking a plane?
5 Who tries to sort out a country's economic problems?
6 What does a babysitter do?
7 When would somebody ask you to hold on?
8 Who looks after the animals in a zoo?

N1	Take *your hat* off	N2	Look for *the keys*	P1	Take *it* off
P2	Look for *them*	Ø	I fell over	G	Give up *smoking*

He was running as hard as he could, but he realised that he was not strong enough to be a good marathon runner. In the distance he could just **make out** the shapes of the leading runners, getting further ahead every minute. 'You'll have to **speed up** if you're going to catch them,' he thought to himself. 'Just **go on**, just keep going.' With every pace he could feel himself **running out of** stamina; he could hardly see the leaders now, and he could no longer **think of** winning. But he would not **give up** without a fight.

Notes

make out	N1 N2 P1	On a cloudy day it is difficult to make things out in the distance.
go on	Ø G	We decided to go on in spite of the rain.
run out of	N2 P2	You run out of strength, stamina, or ideas, when you have no more
run out	Ø	left. You have run out.
think of	P2 G	The runner cannot think of winning.
give up	Ø	The runner will not give up, he will go on to the end.
speed up	N1 N2 P1 Ø	*See Unit 1*

Exercise A

Complete these sentences:

1 The new road will . . . . . . the flow of traffic.
2 What shall we do? I was . . . . . . going to the cinema.
3 Can you give me a light? I've . . . . matches.
4 In the distance he could just . . . . . . the spire of a church.
5 Instead of . . . . . ., you should check your calculations.
6 Have you considered buying a new car? No, I hadn't . . . . . . that.
7 I . . . . What is the answer?
8 Turn left at the traffic lights, take the second right, and then . . . . . . till you reach the church.

Exercise B

Answer these questions:

1 How can you speed a car up?
2 Have you ever thought of taking flying lessons?
3 What would you do if you were faced with an insoluble problem?
4 When would you buy more ink for your pen?
5 What must a driver not do after an accident?
6 What can you make out in the distance?
7 Who first thought of going to the moon?
8 What would a cyclist do after mending a puncture?

N1	Take *your hat* off	N2	Look for *the keys*	P1	Take *it* off
P2	Look for *them*	Ø	I fell over	G	Give up *smoking*

Janice:	It's a good job I **was in** when Alex phoned.
Pamela:	Why?
Janice:	He's invited me out to dinner. He's **picking** me **up** in fifteen minutes. What shall I wear? Do you think I've got time to do my hair? Look, it's ten past already.
Pamela:	Well, **slow down** or you won't be able to do anything.
Janice:	Can you lend me a cigarette? I've **run out**. I must go and **make up** my eyes.
Pamela:	Don't panic so much. Make him wait. At this rate you'll **tire** yourself **out** before he gets here.

Notes

be in	Ø	Janice was in; she was at home.
pick up	N1 N2 P1	Alex would go to Janice's home to pick her up and take her with him.
slow down	N1 N2 P1 Ø	The opposite of speed up.
tire out	N1 N2 P1	You tire a person out. You can say 'I'm tired out,' at the end of a busy day.
run out	Ø	*See Unit 5*
make up	N1 N2 P1 Ø	*See Unit 2*

Exercise A

Complete these sentences:

1 The car . . . . . . as it entered the town.
2 She arranged by telephone to . . . the tickets . . . at the theatre.
3 We'll have to get some more petrol. We've . . . .
4 'Is George there?' 'Hold on. I'll go and see if he . . . .'
5 All this running up and down stairs is beginning to . . . me . . . .
6 I'll get the car and . . . you . . . at the station.
7 I've . . . . inspiration. Can you think of anything we can do?
8 The actress . . . herself . . . to look twenty years younger.

Exercise B

Answer these questions:

1 When is the best time to telephone someone?
2 Name three things that tire you out.
3 Have you ever run out of time in an examination?
4 When does a car slow down?
5 How would you feel after running a marathon?
6 Name three professions in which people make themselves up.
7 What would you pick up at a railway depot?
8 Do you slow down at weekends?

N1	Take *your hat* off	N2	Look for *the keys*	P1	Take *it* off
P2	Look for *them*	Ø	I fell over	G	Give up *smoking*

UNIT 7 *The Government's Energy Policy*

'And therefore I say to the Government, **wake up to** what is happening. It is time we **faced up to** the fact that the country's energy reserves will not last for ever. If we **go on** believing that we are self-sufficient, in ten years' time we shall be in the middle of a very deep recession.

The Government must **work out** a firm policy on energy, suitable for the next twenty years. It must be a policy that will enable us to **keep up** our leading position in the world, and **cope with** the problems of a modern industrial society.'

Notes

wake up to	N2 P2	You wake up to something you hadn't realised before. You wake
wake up	Ø	up and realise it.
face up to	N2 P2	You face up to a difficult situation, if you accept that something must be done about it.
work out	N1 N2 P1	You work out a solution to a problem.
keep up	N1 N2 P1	You keep up your strength or your morale if you prevent it from sinking.
cope with	N2 P2	You cope with a difficult situation or a crisis by trying to do something about it.
go on	Ø G	*See Unit 5*

Exercise A

Complete these sentences:

1 It took him an hour to . . . . . . how to mend the clock.
2 It's about time you . . . . the fact that you've got a family.
3 When he left school, he decided that his languages would be useful and that he should . . . them . . . .
4 Your wife is seeing another man; why don't you . . . . what she is doing?
5 This problem needs a slide rule; if I had one I could . . . it . . . .
6 As the dogs grew bigger, he found it increasingly difficult to . . . . . . them.
7 Why do we always . . . . . . making the same mistakes?
8 Unless we get a grant, it will be difficult to . . . . . . the Abbey and its gardens.

Exercise B

Answer these questions:

1 When there is no more petrol, will people be able to go on driving?
2 Can many people afford to keep up two houses?
3 Name one situation that you could not cope with.
4 Is it easy to work out the meaning of a word you do not know?
5 How does a company face up to a drop in sales?
6 How should you cope with an electrical fire in a building?
7 Do people always wake up to difficult situations before they become worse?
8 How many of the subjects you studied at school have you kept up?

N1	Take *your hat* off	N2	Look for *the keys*	P1	Take *it* off
P2	Look for *them*	Ø	I fell over	G	Give up *smoking*

UNIT 8 *After the Fire*

On the fifth day we returned to London to see how much of the city had survived the fire. The militia and the volunteers were **putting out** the last of the fires, and people were already beginning to **clear up** the rubble and hunt for what remained of their possessions. Here and there we could **make out** the remains of some well-known building, and occasionally we would **come across** a house or church that the fire had miraculously left untouched.

It was clear that a lot of hard work would be needed; the citizens of London would have to **get down to** rebuilding their houses, and the authorities would have to **carry out** a major programme for restoring the city churches.

Notes

clear up N1 N2 P1 Ø   You clear up a mess or a misunderstanding. When a storm is over and the clouds go away you can say, 'It's clearing up.'

come across N2 P2   You come across things or people when you find them by chance.

get down to N2 P2 G   You get down to work, or to doing your work, when you start to concentrate on it.

carry out N2 P1   You carry out a plan when you work following a plan. You carry out a test by testing something.

put out N1 N2 P1   *See Unit 1*

make out N1 N2 P1   *See Unit 5*

Exercise A

Complete these sentences:

1 The fire spread quickly and it took three hours to . . . it . . ..
2 What a beautiful cigarette case. Where did you . . . . . . it?
3 Your handwriting is terrible – I can't . . . it . . . at all.
4 In the years following the war, the Government . . . . . . a major rebuilding programme.
5 Well, I'm glad we've . . . that . . .. It was becoming quite a problem.
6 Several tests were . . . . . . before the drug was put on the market.
7 It's ten o'clock and time you . . . . some work.
8 We'd better . . . . . . this mess before they get here.

Exercise B

Answer these questions:

1 When must doctors carry out tests on patients?
2 When must you not use water to put out a fire?
3 How often do people come across gold in rivers?
4 Name three things you can clear up.
5 What do governments try to do with their policies?
6 When is it difficult to get down to work?
7 When two English people are talking to each other, can you make out what they are saying?
8 How often do you come across people you knew when you were very young?

N1	Take *your hat* off	N2	Look for *the keys*	P1	Take *it* off
P2	Look for *them*	Ø	I fell over	G	Give up *smoking*

Dear Mrs Michaels,

Thank you for **seeing** me **off** at Heathrow Airport last night. We had a pleasant flight, but I was **tired out** when we landed at Rome at five this morning.

My father met me at the airport, and we spent some time **looking round** Rome before returning to Tivoli.

I **picked up** a lot of English during my stay with you, and my father **knows of** somebody who can give me more conversation practice.

I have to **get down to** work soon for my summer examinations, but I am quite confident about my English now.

Thank you again for your hospitality.

Yours, Edoardo.

Notes

see off   N1 N2 P1   You see someone off when you say goodbye to them at the start of their journey.

look round   N2 P2 Ø   You might look round a shop before you buy anything. You can look round a city if you are a tourist.

pick up   N1 N2 P1   Edoardo picked up more English by listening to people than by studying it at school.

know of   N2 P2   Edoardo's father knew of a good teacher although he had never met him.

tire out   N1 N2 P1   *See Unit 6*

get down to   N2 P2 G   *See Unit 8*

Exercise A

Complete these sentences:

1 We asked if we could . . . . . . the antique shop.
2 The flight from Rio to London . . . him . . . .
3 Juan is coming to London? Where did you . . . . . . that bit of news?
4 Do you . . . . . . anywhere I can get my watch repaired quickly?
5 As we had to stop in the village for petrol, we decided to . . . . . . it.
6 We all went to the door to . . . our friends . . . .
7 How is it that you know Portuguese? I . . . it . . . during my holidays.
8 This problem will not disappear until the Government . . . . working out a solution.

Exercise B

Answer these questions:

1 Do you know of any good restaurants in Scotland?
2 How much English would you pick up during a month's holiday in Britain?
3 Where would you see someone off?
4 Name two sports that would tire you out.
5 How would you pick up some idea of the tactics of a particular football team?
6 When do you get down to work in the morning?
7 When would you look round a house?
8 What would you do at the end of a party at your home?

N1 Take *your hat* off	N2 Look for *the keys*	P1 Take *it* off
P2 Look for *them*	Ø I fell over	G Give up *smoking*

UNIT 10 *Espionage*

'How much Russian do you know, Masters?' asked the man called Smith.

'I **picked up** a bit during the War, sir,' replied Masters cautiously.

'Well, I hope you've **kept it up**. You're going to need it. Your trip to Athens **is off**; you're going to Russia instead. Here are your tickets, hotel reservation, false passport, a hundred gold sovereigns, and a detailed map of the embassy. Contact Agent 31 on Thursday at the Cafe Alexei, **carry out** the job on Friday, and get home immediately. If you have any problems, our boys will **look after** you. Any questions?'

'**Hold on**, sir,' said Masters, 'It all sounds very exciting, but I haven't the slightest idea what you're talking about.'

Notes

pick up	N1 N2 P1	*See Unit 9*
keep up	N1 N2 P1	*See Unit 7*
be off	Ø	*See Unit 3*
carry out	N2 P1	*See Unit 8*
look after	N2 P2	*See Unit 4*
hold on	Ø	*See Unit 4*

Exercise A

Complete these sentences:

1 We'll have to get a babysitter to . . . . . . the children.
2 The meeting . . . . because half the delegates have got flu.
3 It looks as though the repairs won't be . . . . . . until spring.
4 During his visit to the factory he . . . . . . some useful information.
5 If the wedding . . . ., what are they going to do with their wedding presents?
6 Would you mind . . . . . . while I go and get your application form?
7 Your exam results were excellent; . . . . . . the good work.
8 The doctor is engaged at the moment. Could you . . . .?

Exercise B

Answer these questions:

1 What is the biggest robbery that has ever been carried out?
2 How can you keep up your knowledge of a language?
3 When would you ask someone to hold on during a telephone conversation?
4 What does a nurse do?
5 In what circumstances would you cancel the invitations to a party?
6 Do you keep up friendships you make on holiday?
7 What knowledge would you pick up by going to auctions?
8 How often should you carry out safety checks on a car?

N1	Take *your hat* off	N2	Look for *the keys*	P1	Take *it* off
P2	Look for *them*	Ø	I fell over	G	Give up *smoking*

George:	Hello, Stan.
Barman:	Hello, George. That sounds like a rotten cold.
George:	Yes, it's terrible. Do you have anything to help me **get rid of** it?
Barman:	Well, you could try firemilk.
George:	What is it? Medicine?
Barman:	No. You put some milk in a pan and stir in cinnamon and brown sugar. You've got to **keep on** stirring so that it doesn't boil, but **wait for** it to get really hot before putting the brandy in.
George:	That sounds good. Did you **make** it **up** yourself?
Barman:	No. I **came across** it in an old recipe book. It may not cure your cold, but at least it'll make you feel good.
George:	Yes, I suppose if I take one of those a day it'll help me **put up with** it till it goes away.

Notes

get rid of	N2 P2	You get rid of a car when you no longer want it, by selling or scrapping it.
wait for	N2 P2	You wait for a bus or a person, or wait for something to happen.
make up	N1 N2 P1	You make up a story or a recipe which did not exist before.
put up with	N2 P2	If you can't get rid of a cold you have to put up with it.
keep on	G	*See Unit 2*
come across	N2 P2	*See Unit 8*

Exercise A

Complete these sentences:

1 He's not here yet; you'll have to . . . . . . him to arrive.
2 He decided to . . . . his motorbike and buy a car.
3 It is not a true story. I . . . it . . . .
4 I . . . . . . a fantastic restaurant near the market.
5 They have been . . . . . . the train for half an hour.
6 The best way to perfect your technique is simply to . . . . . . practising.
7 There were too many workers in the factory so we had to . . . . some of them.
8 He went to the doctor when he could no longer . . . . the pain.

Exercise B

Answer these questions:

1 How can you get rid of a cold?
2 What do people do at a bus-stop?
3 Name two things you have to put up with.
4 What is a lie?
5 Where would you come across a milestone?
6 What can you do about bad weather?
7 If you don't succeed at something the first time, what do you do?
8 Are the stories about King Arthur true or were they made up?

N1	Take *your hat* off	N2	Look for *the keys*	P1	Take *it* off
P2	Look for *them*	Ø	I fell over	G	Give up *smoking*

He really did not know what to **make of** the letter. It was typed clearly and carefully, but without any address or signature. It advised him to **give up** his rights to the piece of land between the bank and the offices at 71 High Street West.

It **struck** him **as** rather odd that anyone unknown to him should **have heard of** his claim to the land, let alone that anyone should go to so much trouble to give him advice.

Or was it advice? Something very strange was **going on**. He decided to **ring up** the police.

Notes

give up	N1 N2 P1	You give up something when you let someone else have it.
strike as	N1 P1	A curious event could strike you as funny, or as being funny.
hear of	N2 P2	This is usually used in a past tense, e.g. 'I had heard of him before I met him.'
go on	Ø	Something strange is going on when something strange is happening.
ring up	N1 N2 P1 Ø	You ring a person up when you phone him or her.
make of	N2 P2	*See Unit 3*

Exercise A

Complete these sentences:

1 You'd better . . . . . . and ask when the coach leaves.
2 Have you . . . . . . the Bermuda Triangle?
3 Yes, I have, but I don't know what to . . . . . . it.
4 With the advances in communication, it isn't difficult to know what is . . . . . . anywhere in the world.
5 He . . . . . . his inheritance to his brother.
6 I don't know what Steve is doing. Why don't you . . . him . . .?
7 Doesn't it . . . you . . . odd that Paula hasn't written?
8 Prince Henry . . . . . . his claim to the throne.

Exercise B

Answer these questions:

1 What is the quickest way to contact a friend abroad?
2 What goes on in summer every four years?
3 Have you heard of John Milton?
4 What do you make of the stories about the yeti?
5 What is going on outside at the moment?
6 When should you give up your seat on a bus?
7 Name something that strikes you as being rather odd.
8 How many Japanese artists have you heard of?

N1	Take *your hat* off	N2	Look for *the keys*	P1	Take *it* off
P2	Look for *them*	Ø	I fell over	G	Give up *smoking*

'Well, lad,' the old man sighed, 'if you can **work out** some way of saving the company, you're welcome to **go ahead** and try. What do you propose to do?' 'Right,' his nephew began, 'it's about time we **looked into** this business of absenteeism. I think paid sick-leave should be limited to one day per month.' 'That's a bit hard on the men, isn't it?'

'Uncle,' the younger man replied, '**I'm all for** good relations between the men and the bosses; but it's time we **faced up to** the facts. Half the men regard sick-leave as paid holiday, and we can **do without** that sort of attitude.'

Notes

go ahead	Ø	This is often used to give permission e.g. 'Can I smoke?' 'Yes, go ahead'.
look into	N2 P2	You look into a problem or a situation that needs resolving when you start to consider it.
be all for	N2 P2	You are all for nuclear disarmament if you support the cause enthusiastically.
do without	N2 P2	We could all do without higher prices. Nobody wants them.
work out	N1 N2 P1	*See Unit 7*
face up to	N2 P2	*See Unit 7*

Exercise A

Complete these sentences:

1 If that's your idea of helping I can . . . . . . it.
2 He is living in a dream world. He doesn't . . . . reality at all.
3 I'll . . . . your suggestions as soon as I have time.
4 They just can't . . . it . . . . You'd better tell them the answer.
5 'May I borrow the power-drill tomorrow?' 'Yes, ...'
6 The doctors cannot . . . . . . what is affecting him.
7 The Government . . . . better relations with neighbouring countries.
8 The management are not . . . . . . with their plans to close the factory.

Exercise B

Answer these questions:

1 Are nuclear weapons really necessary?
2 Name two things you are all for.
3 How can you answer a mathematical problem?
4 What would you do after getting permission to do something?
5 When do you have to face up to the truth?
6 Name three things you could do without.
7 What sort of thing do the police look into?
8 Are you all for cheaper public transport?

N1	Take *your hat* off	N2	Look for *the keys*	P1	Take *it* off
P2	Look for *them*	Ø	I fell over	G	Give up *smoking*

13

Dear Stewart,

Just a short note to thank you and Stella for **putting** us **up** the other night on our way here; and for **seeing** us **off** so early in the morning. We arrived at the cottage late on Monday. It's right at the north tip of Barra and certainly **lives up to** the description we were given. We've spent two days **looking round** the island; it's so beautiful. The cottage is **cut off from** civilisation (the nearest town is five miles away) and we're really glad we **got hold of** it. You'd love it here. See you in three weeks,

Alec and Marjory.

Notes

put up	N1 N2 P1	Alec and Marjory stayed at Stewart and Stella's house. Stewart and Stella put them up.
live up to	N2 P2	A thing or a person lives up to an expectation when that expectation is fulfilled.
cut off from	N1 P1	A person cuts himself off from his friends, if he stops seeing them.
get hold of	N2 P2	Alec and Marjory got hold of the cottage by managing to book it. You can get hold of someone by telephone.
see off	N1 N2 P1	*See Unit 9*
look round	N2 P2 Ø	*See Unit 9*

Exercise A

Complete these sentences:

1 His exam results fully . . . . our expectations.
2 I will go to the station to . . . him . . . .
3 The lighthouse-keeper was . . . . family and friends for two months.
4 The team manager was able to . . . . some new players before the season started.
5 Of course we can . . . you . . . on the night before the party.
6 A narrow channel . . . the island . . . . the mainland.
7 The team did not . . . . its high reputation.
8 We had time to . . . . . . the theatre before the play began.

Exercise B

Answer these questions:

1 Why do people go to an airport when they are not taking a plane?
2 How often do you put someone up?
3 Why do we seldom hear news about Albania?
4 What would you do in an antique shop?
5 How would you get hold of someone's address?
6 How often do racehorses live up to their owners' hopes?
7 If a friend from abroad came to stay where would you see her off when she left?
8 What can you get hold of in a market?

N1	Take *your hat* off	N2	Look for *the keys*	P1	Take *it* off
P2	Look for *them*	Ø	I fell over	G	Give up *smoking*

Lucius **went through** the possibilities in his mind. There were several ways he could **deal with** the threat from the tribal army, but in this unknown country he thought a defensive action from the top of the hill would be the most sensible.

The soldiers and the pack animals **slowed down** as they reached the first slopes of the hill. Lucius looked at the sky; the weather was beginning to **clear up**. In the distance he could hear the wild calls of the enemy. He wondered if he would be able to get his tired legions into position before the rain stopped; already they were **worn out** from pushing the animals.

He **got on** his horse and gave the order to advance up the hill.

Notes

go through	N2 P2	You go through various possible courses of action, trying to find the best. You go through your pockets to find something.
deal with	N2 P2	You deal with a problem or with a person who has a problem when you solve it.
wear out	N1 N2 P1	The men were exhausted; pushing the animals had worn the men out. You also wear out clothes by wearing them a lot.
get on	N2 P2 Ø	You get on a bus, a horse, a bicycle, a train or a plane. When the bus arrived I got on.
slow down	N1 N2 P1 Ø	*See Unit 6*
clear up	N1 N2 P1 Ø	*See Unit 8*

Exercise A

Complete these sentences:

1 He . . . . . . the paper trying to find some news about the robbery.
2 The tyres were . . . . . . after 10,000 miles of driving.
3 After a month's rain the weather at last . . . . . .
4 He . . . . . . the bus when it was still moving.
5 I can't go on; I'm thoroughly . . . .
6 The truck . . . . . . before the traffic lights.
7 Could you . . . . . . this? I'm too busy at the moment.
8 The doctor told him to . . . . . . or he would have a heart attack.

Exercise B

Answer these questions:

1 Where do you get on a bus?
2 How do you feel if you work too hard?
3 What does the weather do after it has stopped raining?
4 What do people who work in a passport office do?
5 What do examiners do with examination scripts?
6 What does a cyclist do when going up a hill?
7 How would you deal with a wasps' nest in your kitchen?
8 What does a teacher do with a pupil's homework?

N1 Take *your hat* off	N2 Look for *the keys*	P1 Take *it* off
P2 Look for *them*	Ø I fell over	G Give up *smoking*

15

Do you have difficulty in **speaking out** in public? Do you find it hard to **cope with** situations that require responsibility?

Being On Top is the answer to your problems. *Being On Top* is a new book that shows you how to control your emotions, how to **get rid of** your fears, how to **find out** what **lies behind** your inability to make people respect you. And a new set of exercises will show you how to develop those qualities of leadership which bring health, wealth, success and happiness.

Send away for *Being On Top* today.

Notes

speak out	Ø	I didn't want to accuse him, but I couldn't restrain myself. I had to speak out.
find out	N1 N2 P1 Ø	You find out what time it is by looking at your watch.
lie behind	N2 P2	An explanation of some kind lies behind something confusing.
send away for	N2 P2	You send away for something you see advertised in a magazine if you order it by post.
cope with	N2 P2	*See Unit 7*
get rid of	N2 P2	*See Unit 11*

Exercise A

Complete these sentences:

1 I can't . . . . . . your mistakes any longer.
2 Pass me the telephone directory and I'll . . . . . . where he lives.
3 When he won some money he was able to . . . . his debts.
4 She saw an advertisement for cheap radios and decided to . . . . one.
5 We'll have to employ more staff to . . . . . . the new work.
6 The new member . . . . . . against the Government's actions in Parliament.
7 I think some rather dubious financial dealings . . . . . . the company's curious policy.
8 Simon's getting married? When did you . . . that . . .?

Exercise B

Answer these questions:

1 Name three things you could send away for.
2 What do you use a train timetable for?
3 Does political theory always lie behind a government's actions?
4 How would you cope with a burst water pipe?
5 In what circumstances would you speak out?
6 How can you find out how to play cricket?
7 How do you get rid of toothache?
8 How can you buy something you see advertised in a magazine?

N1	Take *your hat* off	N2	Look for *the keys*	P1	Take *it* off
P2	Look for *them*	Ø	I fell over	G	Give up *smoking*

Michael:	Steve. Have you **heard of** Prospect Hill?
Steve:	No. What is it?
Michael:	I'll show you. It's a hill in the forest with a fantastic view. Do you want to bring your camera?
Steve:	Sounds great. Have you got your tripod?
Michael:	No, but we can **drop in** at my house and **pick** it **up** on the way. What are you **looking for**?
Steve:	The light meter. I must have put it somewhere.
Michael:	Well, **hurry up**. We'll have to **set off** soon or the light will disappear altogether.

Notes

drop in	Ø	If you visit someone, you drop in. You drop in at someone's home to visit him, or drop in on him.
drop in at	N2	
drop in on	N2 P2	
look for	N2 P2	You look for someone, when you want to find him.
hurry up	Ø	This is usually used in conversation e.g. Hurry up or we'll miss the bus.
set off	Ø	At the beginning of a journey you set off.
hear of	N2 P2	*See Unit 12*
pick up	N1 N2 P1	*See Unit 6*

Exercise A

Complete these sentences:

1 Why don't you . . . . . . and see us on your way back from work?
2 They will have to . . . . . . if they want to get to the church on time.
3 We could . . . . . . the wine on the afternoon of the party.
4 It's ridiculous. I've never . . . . . . anything so stupid in my whole life.
5 He spent hours . . . . . . somewhere to eat.
6 I think we should . . . . . . at nine to get there by ten.
7 Where have you been? I've been . . . . . . you all over the place.
8 I'll . . . . . . at the surgery and see if my prescription is ready.

Exercise B

Answer these questions:

1 What do you do at the beginning of a journey?
2 When would you drop in on someone?
3 What would you do if you were late?
4 How many British cities have you heard of?
5 Where would you look for a dinosaur?
6 How often do people drop in at your home?
7 Why does a train stop at stations before its final destination?
8 If you lost your car keys, what would be the first thing you would do?

N1	Take *your hat* off	N2	Look for *the keys*	P1	Take *it* off
P2	Look for *them*	Ø	I fell over	G	Give up *smoking*

17

UNIT 18 *A Driving Lesson*

'No. **Wait for** the lights to go green before you **go ahead**.

No, don't stop now – **carry on**. It's not a good idea to stop in the middle of the road. Never mind.

Now, I want you to turn left at the next crossroads. Keep both your hands on the wheel. Now you can indicate. Don't **run** the old man **over**.

Would you like to try a three-point turn? Not today? O.K. then.

You can **turn** the indicator **off** now. We don't need it anymore.

All right, you can stop here.

Yes, I think you could **do with** a few more lessons before you take your test.'

Notes

carry on	Ø G	You can carry on, or carry on with what you are doing when you
carry on with	N2 P2	continue or start again.
run over	N1 N2 P1 P2	You run over a pedestrian or an animal if you hit one when you are driving.
turn off	N1 N2 P1 Ø	You turn off the television or the light before going to bed.
do with	N2 P2	On a hot day you might say 'I could do with a cold drink'.
wait for	N2 P2	*See Unit 11*
go ahead	Ø	*See Unit 13*

Exercise A

Complete these sentences:

1 I think I . . . . . . a rabbit the other night.
2 This room could . . . . . . a thorough cleaning.
3 He shouldn't have . . . . . . writing after the examination had finished.
4 The audience sat in their seats and . . . . . . the play to start.
5 This job is too hard for me. I reckon I could . . . . . . a change.
6 . . . the lights . . . when you leave the school.
7 If the doctor tells you not to smoke, you shouldn't . . . . . . doing it.
8 The Council told him that he could . . . . . . and restore the old house.

Exercise B

Answer these questions:

1 What could a dusty house do with?
2 What do you do when you have finished watching television?
3 What might happen if you ran across a busy road without looking?
4 When would you go ahead and do something?
5 How long do you usually have to wait for a bus?
6 Name four things you could do with.
7 What is the last thing you do at night?
8 Do you think that people will carry on using petrol till the end of the next century?

N1 Take *your hat* off	N2 Look for *the keys*	P1 Take *it* off
P2 Look for *them*	Ø I fell over	G Give up *smoking*

18

'Well, that's a bit odd,' said Sheila.

'What?' I asked.

'That phone call,' she replied. 'I don't know who it was. He was talking about something I couldn't understand, and then he just **broke off** in mid-sentence and **hung up**.'

'Maybe he realised he had **mistaken** you **for** someone else,' I **pointed out**.

'No doubt something simple **lies behind** it,' she replied, going over to the window. 'But doesn't it **strike** you **as** a bit odd that it's the third time this week that it's happened?'

Notes

break off	Ø	In the middle of his lecture he broke off to drink some water.
hang up	Ø	At the end of a telephone conversation you hang up.
mistake for	N1 P1	You can mistake one thing or person for another e.g. 'I beg your pardon; I mistook you for my sister.'
point out	N1 N2 P1	You point out something to someone who has not seen it.
lie behind	N2 P2	*See Unit 16*
strike as	N1 P1	*See Unit 12*

Exercise A

Complete these sentences:

1 I wonder what . . . . . . his strange behaviour.
2 He . . . . . . in mid-sentence and stared past my shoulder.
3 She . . . . . . something he had overlooked.
4 If you hadn't been here, I would have . . . it . . . a genuine antique.
5 I would never have noticed the fault if you had not . . . it . . . to me.
6 She . . . . . . before I could apologise.
7 I'm sorry; I . . . your umbrella . . . mine.
8 The fact that there was a dead bird on the doorstep . . . me . . . rather curious.

Exercise B

Answer these questions:

1 When would you hang up?
2 Does it strike you as odd that there are no detailed photographs of the Loch Ness Monster?
3 What explanation do you think lies behind the story of the Loch Ness Monster?
4 What does a tourist guide do?
5 Have you ever been mistaken for someone else?
6 When would you break off during a conversation?
7 Is it easy to mistake a peach for an apricot?
8 At the end of a telephone conversation, do you usually hang up before the other person?

N1	Take *your hat* off	N2	Look for *the keys*	P1	Take *it* off
P2	Look for *them*	Ø	I fell over	G	Give up *smoking*

If you are **looking for** somewhere to have a motoring holiday, we **know of** no better place than Cornwall.

Cornwall contains some of England's most beautiful scenery, with its wild hills, clean beaches, old castles and half-forgotten villages. There are plenty of places to stay; small hotels and bed and breakfasts will **put** you **up** for as little as £10.00 a night. In the summer there is a lot **going on**, or, if you prefer sunbathing, Cornwall's weather is the warmest in Britain.

Send away for our brochure *Holidays in Cornwall* today. And we promise, Cornwall will **live up to** your every expectation.

Notes

look for	N2	P2	*See Unit 17*
know of	N2	P2	*See Unit 9*
put up	N1 N2	P1	*See Unit 14*
go on	Ø		*See Unit 12*
send away for	N2	P2	*See Unit 16*
live up to	N2	P2	*See Unit 14*

Exercise A

Complete these sentences:

1 After reading the advertisement for Californian wine, he decided to . . . . some.
2 What's been . . . . . . here? Who made all this mess?
3 His parents' standards were so high that he had trouble . . . . them.
4 This is a very rare illness, but I . . . . . . a doctor who may be able to help you.
5 I don't like this at all. Something nasty is . . . .
6 If you're . . . . . . a way to avoid your responsibilities, I can tell you now that there isn't one.
7 As you are coming to dinner, why not stay the night? We can easily . . . you . . . .
8 Do you . . . . . . anywhere that I can get a bed for the night?

Exercise B

Answer these questions:

1 Do holiday hotels always live up to the travel agents' brochures?
2 What goes on at the Edinburgh Festival every summer?
3 Do you know of anywhere that has colder winters than Britain?
4 If you wanted to buy a house, how would you look for a suitable one?
5 When would someone put you up?
6 How can you find out what is going on around the world?
7 What is mail order shopping?
8 If a customs officer searched your luggage, what would he be looking for?

N1	Take *your hat* off	N2	Look for *the keys*	P1	Take *it* off
P2	Look for *them*	Ø	I fell over	G	Give up *smoking*

'So I think we should go on strike and show the managers who is really important – the boss or the worker.'

'No, George, you're making a big mistake. It's much better to **build up** good relations with the managers, even if it does happen slowly.'

'Oh, **I'm all for** a happy atmosphere. Did I ever say I wasn't?'

'No, but we've got enough money to **get by** at the moment. I know you want more than the minimum, but you're **asking for** too much. These are hard times, and we've just got to **put up with** them.'

'I agree that we've got enough money now; but what happens when prices **go up** again?'

Notes

build up	N1 N2 P1	A weak man can build up his strength and become a boxer.
get by	Ø	They may be poor, but they have enough money to get by. They
get by on	N2 P2	can get by on what they have.
ask for	N2 P2	You can ask for money, a drink, a chance or more time.
go up	Ø	Prices or wages go up. In summer the temperature goes up.
be all for	N2 P2	*See Unit 13*
put up with	N2 P2	*See Unit 11*

Exercise A

Complete these sentences:

1 He trained for three weeks before the race to . . . . . . his energy.
2 If prices . . . . . . again we shall lose all our business.
3 They were not rich, but they had enough money to . . . .
4 . . . the examiner . . . more paper if you need it.
5 Over the years he had . . . . . . quite a profitable business.
6 That's enough! I don't see why I should . . . . this noise any longer.
7 The shop is just about to close. Do we need more milk or can we . . . . what we have?
8 The union are . . . . . . better working conditions in the factory.

Exercise B

Answer these questions:

1 Can you put up with a lot of noise?
2 Why do athletes sometimes train in the mountains?
3 Are you all for a reduction in tax?
4 How much money do you need per week to get by?
5 How often does the price of petrol go up?
6 What does a beggar do?
7 What happens to the temperature in summer?
8 During a meal in a restaurant, when would you call the waiter?

N1 Take *your hat* off	N2 Look for *the keys*	P1 Take *it* off
P2 Look for *them*	Ø I fell over	G Give up *smoking*

When Carfield United lost their twentieth match in a row, the board of directors met to **look into** the club's problems. They **went through** the accounts and found that fewer supporters had been coming to matches. The club was beginning to lose money and the situation was becoming desperate. During the course of the discussion Alexis Dani's name **came up**. Though he was secure in his job as manager of a team at the other end of the country, he might just be persuaded to **take over**.

But then some clouds appeared on the horizon. It was known that Dani had strong family connections in the South and even stronger career ambitions. It seemed that he might just **turn** the opportunity **down** because it did not **fit in with** his plans.

Notes

come up	Ø	Dani's name came up during the discussion. They were talking about the situation and his name was mentioned.
take over	N1 N2 P1 Ø	They wanted Dani to take over and become the new manager.
turn down	N1 N2 P1	Dani would turn the job down if he didn't want it.
fit in with	N2 P2	The job would not fit in with his plans, as he had already arranged to stay in the South.
look into	N2 P2	*See Unit 13*
go through	N2 P2	*See Unit 15*

Exercise A

Complete these sentences:

1 As she did not want to get married, she . . . . his offer.
2 When the manager was taken ill, the assistant manager . . . .
3 Since you think this matter is so important, I'll . . . . it.
4 I'll be late home tonight – something rather important has . . . .
5 When he had finished the work, he . . . . . . it, looking for mistakes.
6 At six o'clock the invading soldiers . . . . the town.
7 He did not go on holiday with her, as it did not . . . . his plans.
8 If their offer of a job is not satisfactory you should . . . it . . ..

Exercise B

Answer these questions:

1 In what circumstances would you cancel something another person had arranged for you?
2 What does a vice-chairman do when the chairman is ill?
3 How often does a word you don't know come up when you're reading an English book?
4 When would you go through a newspaper?
5 What sort of thing would a private detective look into?
6 When would you turn an invitation down?
7 What does a teacher do with homework?
8 Do you have to arrange your holidays to fit in with those of anyone else?

N1	Take *your hat* off	N2	Look for *the keys*	P1	Take *it* off
P2	Look for *them*	Ø	I fell over	G	Give up *smoking*

After the storm we surveyed the damage to the yacht. There was a lot of water **pouring in** through a large hole below the water-line. There were two alternatives: we could either stay with the boat and wait until a rescue helicopter **turned up**, or gather as much food as possible and try to swim to the island about a mile away. Eventually we **decided on** the latter, as the sea was threatening to **tear** our yacht **apart**.

The island, as well as being totally **cut off from** the outside world, had no fresh water. We reckoned that we would be able to **do without** food, but if we were not rescued within four days we would be in real trouble.

Notes

pour in	Ø	Water poured in through the hole. It poured into the boat. Money
pour into	N2 P2	pours in after an appeal.
turn up	Ø	The helicopter would not definitely come, but they hoped it would turn up.
decide on	N2 P2	Faced with two alternatives, they decided on one.
tear apart	N1 P1	The sea would tear the boat apart. Civil war tears a country apart.
do without	N2 P2	As long as they had water, they would be able to do without food.
cut off from	N1 P1	*See Unit 14*

Exercise A

Complete these sentences:

1 He was faced with a number of possible partners, and eventually he . . . . Jan.
2 I . . . . when they were least expecting me.
3 The mountaineers left behind all the things they could . . . .
4 When the doors were opened the people . . . .
5 He lived for a while in a monastery, ... the world.
6 He could feel the oxygen . . . . . . his lungs from the canister on his back.
7 A dispute over Arthur's will . . . the family . . ..
8 If need be, we can . . . . a holiday this year.

Exercise B

Answer these questions:

1 Name three things you cannot do without.
2 Is an island always cut off from the mainland?
3 Do you ever turn up late for work?
4 What would you do if you had to choose between two alternatives?
5 When do people pour into a shop?
6 What could a heavy storm do to a ship?
7 What could tear a country apart?
8 What is life like for a lighthouse keeper?

N1	Take *your hat* off	N2	Look for *the keys*	P1	Take *it* off
P2	Look for *them*	Ø	I fell over	G	Give up *smoking*

'The Government regrets that discussions with the General Workers' Union have been **broken off**. However, in reply to the Honourable Member I have **looked through** the information regarding agricultural imports and exports which, compared to the official statistics, seems to be, shall we say, inaccurate. Indeed, one could, with some justification, say that he has **made** most of it **up**. So I repeat, huge wage claims will **put back** our campaign against inflation. Inflation is this country's number one enemy. The Government **speaks for** the majority of the electorate, and the people will not **stand for** inflation in wages or prices.'

Notes

break off N1 N2 P1 — The management broke off discussions with the union because they could not agree. A couple would break off an engagement when they no longer wanted to marry each other.

look through N2 P2 — You look through something written when you read it for a general impression or to check it quickly.

put back N1 N2 P1 P2 — A delay puts back your plans. If you gambled all your savings, and lost, it would put you back where you started.

speak for N2 P2 — An elected representative speaks for the people who elected him.

stand for N2 P2 — This is usually used in the negative. Referees in games will not stand for any illegal play.

make up N1 N2 P1 — *See Unit 11*

Exercise A

Complete these sentences:

1 This is intolerable! I won't . . . . . . it.
2 The delay . . . us . . . two and a half hours.
3 Hans Christian Andersen . . . . . . some of the world's best loved tales.
4 He . . . . . . the paper on his way to work.
5 The strikers elected a spokesman to . . . . . . them.
6 The two countries . . . . . . diplomatic relations, and two days later were at war.
7 I know that's not true. You've . . . it . . . .
8 The judge said that he would not . . . . . . disturbance in the court.

Exercise B

Answer these questions:

1 Do you always read a newspaper thoroughly?
2 What does a delegate do?
3 When do people put their clocks back?
4 Name two things you would not stand for.
5 Do playwrights always make up the stories of their plays?
6 Do you look through the post when it arrives?
7 When would countries break off diplomatic relations?
8 Who speaks for a country in international meetings?

N1	Take *your hat* off	N2	Look for *the keys*	P1	Take *it* off
P2	Look for *them*	Ø	I fell over	G	Give up *smoking*

Mark:	Hello, operator? I've been trying to **ring up** a friend of mine, but the number has been engaged for three hours. The number is 50473.
Operator:	And you can't **get through**, you say?
Mark:	That's right. The phone seems to be permanently engaged.
Operator:	Could you hold the line, please. I'll just **find out** whether the subscriber has been **cut off**.
Mark:	Why should that happen?
Operator:	Maybe the bill has not been paid.
Mark:	I see. Well, it must be a new number because he **moved in** only last week.
Operator:	In that case the receiver may not be placed on the phone properly. I'll contact the engineer. Try **calling back** in an hour or two.
Mark:	O.K. Thank you.

Notes

get through	Ø	When you try to phone someone, if the line is busy or out of order,
get through to	N2 P2	you cannot get through to him.
cut off	N1 N2 P1	If the telephone bill is not paid, engineers cut the phone or the subscriber off.
move in	Ø	When you go to live in a new house, you move in. You move into
move into	N2 P2	a new flat.
call back	N1 P1 Ø	You call back if you cannot get through first time.
ring up	N1 N2 P1 Ø	*See Unit 12*
find out	N1 N2 P1 Ø	*See Unit 16*

Exercise A

Complete these sentences:

1 I looked in the directory to . . . . . . what her number was.
2 When we left the house, the Electricity Department . . . . the power.
3 We . . . . . . as soon as the house was ready.
4 I'll . . . you . . . when I have more time to talk.
5 I'm not sure if the phone is working. I can't . . . .
6 Is Francis coming? Let's . . . him . . . and see.
7 Gas seemed to be escaping, so the engineer . . . it . . . .
8 They asked me to . . . . . . in an hour, when they would have the information.

Exercise B

Answer these questions:

1 Who first found out that the world was round?
2 When would the authorities cut your water supply off?
3 What would someone do after buying a flat?
4 If you tried to phone someone who was out, what would you do?
5 What is a telephone for?
6 What do you use an encyclopedia for?
7 What would happen if your friend's phone was out of order?
8 Name three things which could be cut off.

N1	Take *your hat* off	N2	Look for *the keys*	P1	Take *it* off
P2	Look for *them*	Ø	I fell over	G	Give up *smoking*

It was five o'clock on a fine May morning. Shakespeare mounted his horse and **set off**, hoping to reach Oxford before nightfall. Around him, the streets of London were coming to life as the apprentices took the wooden shutters from the windows.

'All this travelling between Stratford and London will **wear** me **out**,' thought William. 'I wish I could **give** it **up** and settle for good in one place or the other. But Anne doesn't like it here and there's no playhouse in Stratford.'

This time he had had to stay a week longer than expected, but he had bought his family some special gifts to **make up for** it. 'They'll **get over** it as soon as they see me. It will **turn out** all right I'm sure.'

Notes

give up	N1 N2 P1 G	You can give up smoking, drinking or give up a job if you stop doing it.
make up for	N2 P2 G	An unexpected success makes up for a failure.
get over	N2 P2	When something no longer causes you pain, you say 'I have got over it.'
turn out	Ø	Things turn out well or badly. They can turn out to be all right or dangerous or a good thing.
set off	Ø	*See Unit 17*
wear out	N1 N2 P1	*See Unit 15*

Exercise A

Complete these sentences:

1 Her success in the 200 metres . . . . her failure to qualify for the 100 metres.
2 His mother died and it took him a year to . . . . . . it.
3 The girl he had never seen before . . . . . . to be his cousin.
4 The party of explorers . . . . for the lost city early in the morning.
5 You'll have to . . . . cricket if you want to get your degree.
6 Look at your shoes. You've . . . them . . . .
7 He'll have to work hard to . . . . the time he lost.
8 He arrived late, but things . . . . all right, because so did everyone else.

Exercise B

Answer these questions:

1 Is it easy to give up smoking?
2 Name two things which can wear a machine out.
3 How long would it take you to get over an electric shock?
4 What sets off from a port?
5 Do exam results always turn out to be satisfactory?
6 If you missed a week's work through illness, would you try to make up for it?
7 Name two things you could not give up doing.
8 How can nurses help people to get over the effects of rheumatism?

N1	Take *your hat* off	N2	Look for *the keys*	P1	Take *it* off
P2	Look for *them*	Ø	I fell over	G	Give up *smoking*

'Poor Jonathan. He looks so unhappy just sitting in his flat by himself.'

'I think he's quite content surrounded by his things. He's always been a great collector.'

'Is that what you call it? I'd say he's just never **thrown** anything **away**. The place needs **tidying up**. It's a terrible mess. He never **washes up**.'

'No. He doesn't really **take** much **care of** himself, either. He never eats properly and he smokes far too much.'

'Maybe we should **get hold of** a housekeeper for him.'

'Or a wife. Come on, let's go to the pub.'

'Yes, I could **do with** a drink.'

Notes

throw away N1 N2 P1 You can throw away something you don't want. You throw rubbish away.

tidy up N1 N2 P1 Ø You can tidy up a mess. When my desk is untidy I tidy it up.

wash up N1 N2 P1 Ø After a meal you wash up when you wash the dishes.

take care of N2 P2 You can take care of yourself or a precious object. A nurse takes care of an invalid.

get hold of N2 P2 *See Unit 14*

do with N2 P2 *See Unit 18*

Exercise A

Complete these sentences:

1 . . . . that watch: it was my grandfather's.
2 I could . . . . . . something to eat. I haven't had anything all day.
3 After the party, we . . . the glasses . . . .
4 I do wish you'd . . . your room . . . sometimes.
5 When I had finished reading the pamphlet, I . . . it . . . .
6 The management . . . . some superb entertainers for the cabaret.
7 Let's share the work: I'll cook and you . . . . . . afterwards.
8 It took a long time to . . . . after the children's visit.

Exercise B

Answer these questions:

1 What do you do after a meal?
2 What would you do after a party?
3 Can you throw away a car?
4 What do zoo keepers do?
5 What would a tired and busy person want?
6 What do you do with yesterday's newspaper?
7 How would you get hold of a costume for a fancy dress party?
8 What does a bodyguard do?

N1	Take *your hat* off	N2	Look for *the keys*	P1	Take *it* off
P2	Look for *them*	Ø	I fell over	G	Give up *smoking*

Caligula's excesses **tore** Rome **apart**; his followers led a life of absolute luxury, while others were afraid to **speak out**, for fear of the secret police.

Daily, people were **taken away** from their families to work in the mines. Few, if any, of them ever returned. The people in their misery, **longed for** a just and decent emperor. But Caligula seemed to be above the law; he could **get away with** anything. And the people of Rome had no one to **turn to** for help.

Notes

take away	N1 N2 P1	In a hamburger restaurant you either sit down to eat your food, or you take it away.
long for	N2 P2	You long for something you want very much.
get away with	N2 P2 G	Caligula could not be prosecuted. He committed illegal acts and got away with them.
turn to	N2 P2	You turn to someone you want help from.
tear apart	N1 P1	*See Unit 23*
speak out	Ø	*See Unit 16*

Exercise A

Complete these sentences:

1 When he needed money, he always . . . . . . his father.
2 The policeman who had been shot shouted, 'You'll never . . . . this.'
3 After the trial, the prisoner was . . . . and led to prison.
4 A lot of people . . . . . . against the Governor's injustice.
5 A month of rioting . . . the city . . . .
6 In a situation like yours, I would . . . . . . the priest for help.
7 I have always . . . . . . the opportunity of flying a plane myself.
8 At last! I've been . . . . . . a chance to meet you.

Exercise B

Answer these questions:

1 What happens when a criminal is not caught?
2 Which drug can be used to take away pain?
3 Have you ever found yourself longing for a holiday?
4 Who would you turn to if you needed financial help?
5 What could a tornado do?
6 Would you speak out in a discussion if you knew everyone would disagree with you?
7 Describe a situation in which you got away with something.
8 How often do you buy food from a take-away restaurant?

N1	Take *your hat* off	N2	Look for *the keys*	P1	Take *it* off
P2	Look for *them*	Ø	I fell over	G	Give up *smoking*

UNIT 29 *Golden Meadow Margarine*

Look at these two slices of bread.
Could you **pick out** which one has butter on it, and which has
Golden Meadow margarine?
Well, here's your chance. Next time you **drop in at** your local
supermarket, **look out for** our girls. They will be there with plates
just like this one. We put butter on one slice of bread and *Golden
Meadow* on the other. If you can **tell** *Golden Meadow* **from** butter, you
can **stock up with** a week's supply of groceries at our expense.
Golden Meadow margarine; you'll **mistake** it **for** butter!

Notes

pick out	N1 N2 P1	The person in the shop has to pick out the slice of bread with margarine on it. The idea is to select the correct one.
look out for	N2 P2	While you are doing something, you can look out for something else, e.g. while you are checking an essay you look out for mistakes.
tell from	N1 P1	If the margarine is very like butter, it is hard to tell it from butter.
stock up with	N2 P2	People stock up with food if the shops are going to close for a few days.
drop in at	N2	*See Unit 17*
mistake for	N1 P1	*See Unit 19*

Exercise A

Complete these sentences:

1 I think the twins are identical. I certainly
  can't . . . Jane . . . Alice.
2 Michele has . . . . . . a couple of films she
  wants you to get tickets for.
3 I'll . . . . . . and collect the books this
  evening.
4 Could you . . . . a children's
  dictionary when you go to the city?
5 Before the holiday, she . . . .
  frozen food.
6 It is easy to . . . a painting by Rubens . . .
  one by Rembrandt.
7 She went to look for dresses that would suit
  her, and eventually . . . . . . a couple.
8 I think we'd better . . . . sugar
  before they put the price up again.

Exercise B

Answer these questions:

1 Have you ever mistaken your coat for
  someone else's?
2 What do people do before a fuel shortage?
3 How can you tell an African elephant from
  an Indian elephant?
4 What do people pick out in a library?
5 What would you look out for while crossing
  the road?
6 Why would you drop in at a florist's shop
  on your way home?
7 How can you tell French wine from Italian
  wine?
8 What do people look out for in markets?

N1	Take *your hat* off	N2	Look for *the keys*	P1	Take *it* off
P2	Look for *them*	Ø	I fell over	G	Give up *smoking*

'So you will publish the manuscript, then?' Stewart could hardly believe his ears.

'We are prepared to give you two pence per copy sold. Publishing poetry is a great risk for . . .'

'Two pence!' shouted Stewart. 'I must have enough money to let me **carry on** writing.'

Mr Walpole sighed, 'As I **pointed out** to you last week when you **asked for** an advance, poetry is a great risk.'

'How can I buy food with two pence a copy sold?'

'Mr Allen, how many publishers **turned down** your manuscript? Twelve, I believe. Do not **throw away** this opportunity. It may be your last.'

'But two pence a copy!'

'**Call back** next week, Mr Allen. I'll see what I can do.'

Notes

throw away	N1 N2 P1	If you do not make full use of an opportunity, you throw it away.
call back	Ø	Used without a pronoun; Mr Allen is asked to call back, in person.
carry on	Ø G	*See Unit 18*
point out	N1 N2 P1	*See Unit 19*
ask for	N2 P2	*See Unit 21*
turn down	N1 N2 P1	*See Unit 22*

Exercise A

Complete these sentences:

1 He . . . . . . driving even though he had lost his licence.
2 James . . . the boss . . . a chance to show what he could do.
3 I . . . . . . that there was an objection to her plan.
4 There's no hope now. That was my last chance and I've . . . it . . . .
5 Your parcel may arrive tomorrow. . . . . . . and see.
6 The visiting team . . . . . . their lead by not concentrating on the game.
7 Don't forget that I . . . . . . four offers of marriage before I accepted you.
8 The archaeologist . . . . . . the shape of the building to the students.

Exercise B

Answer these questions:

1 Why would you turn an offer of a job down?
2 If your doctor took some X-rays of you, why would you call back?
3 Why should you not throw away an opportunity to do something you want to do?
4 What does a guide do in a museum?
5 What are the first and last things you would ask for in a restaurant?
6 Would you carry on drinking if a doctor told you to stop?
7 Name two things you could turn down.
8 What does a ticket inspector ask you for?

N1	Take *your hat* off	N2	Look for *the keys*	P1	Take *it* off
P2	Look for *them*	Ø	I fell over	G	Give up *smoking*

'So Mr Pepper, what do you see happening to the Western Motor Company in the next few years?'

'I think we have **broken through** a major barrier, by **drawing up** an agreement with the Unions regarding new technology. With new technology we can **get on with** the job of producing high quality cars at a remarkably low cost.'

'This agreement is very important to you and the company.'

'Indeed it is. The fact that we have this agreement certainly **makes up for** the time we lost through the strike. New orders are **pouring in** every day and our shareholders can **look forward to** very high dividends this year.'

Notes

break through	N2 P2	You break through a barrier of some kind. You can speak of a breakthrough e.g. the discovery of penicillin was a breakthrough in science.
draw up	N1 N2 P1	You draw up a plan, an agreement or a document when you prepare it.
get on with	N2 P2	After a break you get on with your work. When you do a job without being interrupted you get on with it.
look forward to	N2 P2 G	People who work hard during the week look forward to weekends. They think about the weekend during the week.
make up for	N2 P2 G	*See Unit 26*
pour in	Ø	*See Unit 23*

Exercise A

Complete these sentences:

1 He told me to stop reading the magazine and . . . . my work.
2 The water . . . . through a hole in the roof when the rain began.
3 Jane lost her necklace, but her father bought her another to . . . . it.
4 I'm really . . . . seeing Bill on Friday.
5 We may assume that one day there will be a . . . in cancer research.
6 They will . . . . the rebuilding as soon as the plans are ready.
7 Did you do the design yourself or did you get an architect to . . . it . . .?
8 Nothing seems to be able to annoy him or . . . . his calm exterior.

Exercise B

Answer these questions:

1 Do you look forward to Friday nights?
2 What does an architect do?
3 What would you do after taking a break from something?
4 If you lost your wallet, what could make up for it?
5 What happens just as a boat sinks?
6 Describe something you are looking forward to.
7 At what speed does a plane break through the sound barrier?
8 What would a government do to make up for increased spending?

N1	Take *your hat* off	N2	Look for *the keys*	P1	Take *it* off
P2	Look for *them*	Ø	I fell over	G	Give up *smoking*

31

Minckowicz's new book, *Dreaming*, which **comes out** tomorrow, is about an adolescent **growing up** in the sixties in San Francisco. As a child he finds it difficult to **join in** the games of other children and, on leaving school, decides that he does not **fit in with** the society that previous generations have created. He argues with his parents, experiments with drugs, and before long has **dropped out of** college and gone to live in a commune. Here, however, he finds himself **longing for** the 'Great American Dream' into which he was born. *Dreaming* shows Minckowicz's skill in the observation of detail, and his use of imagery. Those who enjoyed *Summer Songs* and *Old Story* will find this book delightful.

Notes

come out	Ø	A book, a film or a magazine comes out when it is published or released. Newspapers come out every day.
grow up	Ø	During your childhood you grow up in a city, or in a family.
join in	N2 Ø	The child found it difficult to join in the games, because the others didn't like him.
drop out of	N2 P2	The adolescent dropped out of college. He dropped out and no
drop out	Ø	longer went to classes.
fit in with	N2 P2	*See Unit 22*
long for	N2 P2	*See Unit 28*

Exercise A

Complete these sentences:

1 No daily papers . . . . . . on Sundays in Britain.
2 He is the odd man out; he doesn't seem to . . . . the rest of the group.
3 Why don't you . . . . . .? We need another player for the team.
4 He had cramp in his leg, so he decided to . . . . the race.
5 Why doesn't he . . . . and act like an adult?
6 It's beautiful. I've always . . . . . . a watch like this.
7 If you want to get a flat through the evening paper, you'll have to buy a copy as soon as it . . . .
8 It's a good idea but, sadly, it does not . . . . the rest of our plans.

Exercise B

Answer these questions:

1 Do you long for the day when everybody speaks the same language?
2 How many editions of this book have come out?
3 Name two things you can join in.
4 What do people do between the ages of 12 and 18?
5 Could you give three reasons why someone should drop out of college?
6 Why does one of these languages not fit in with the others: Italian, Spanish, Arabic, French?
7 Where did you grow up?
8 What sort of game could spectators join in?

N1	Take *your hat* off	N2	Look for *the keys*	P1	Take *it* off
P2	Look for *them*	Ø	I fell over	G	Give up *smoking*

■ UNIT 33 *Recovering from an Accident* ■

When Alec broke his leg a year before the Olympics, the accident **put** his training programme **back** a few months. Previously he was swimming two miles a day, hoping to **build up** to five miles just before the Games, but now he could just manage a hundred yards or so before the pain became too much. Now he doubted whether he would be able to **catch up with** his schedule in time to qualify for the Games.

It was a stupid accident. A car had not stopped at a pedestrian crossing and had **knocked** him **down**. Alec **went through** a bad time and got very depressed in hospital, but his trainer encouraged him, and he **pulled himself together** and started swimming again.

Notes

catch up with	N2 P2	Slower runners in a race try to catch up with the leader. They try
catch up	N1 P1 Ø	to catch him up.
knock down	N1 N2 P1	A car can knock a person down in an accident.
go through	N2 P2	When life becomes difficult, you go through a difficult time.
pull yourself together	P1	Only used with pronouns ending in —self. After going through a period of illness, a person could pull himself together and help himself to get better.
put back	N1 N2 P1 P2	*See Unit 24*
build up	N1 N2 P1	*See Unit 21*

Exercise A

Complete these sentences:

1 Due to a fault in the design we have had to . . . . . . the launch of the new car about six months.
2 You will have to work harder if you want to . . . . the other students in the class.
3 The bus went out of control and . . . . two people.
4 After two months' convalescence he decided to . . . himself . . . and return to work.
5 During the recession the country . . . . a very bad time.
6 She left the shop and ran to . . . . her friends.
7 Weight-lifting exercises should help you to . . . your strength . . . .
8 I think he . . . . a lot of pain before his operation.

Exercise B

Answer these questions:

1 Have you ever been knocked down by a car?
2 What would a delay do to you?
3 Name three things you could build up.
4 What would you have to do if you were behind in your work?
5 When would someone tell you to pull yourself together?
6 Would you go through a lot of pain before going to the dentist?
7 Why do people go jogging?
8 What do people suffering from shock try to do?

N1	Take *your hat* off	N2	Look for *the keys*	P1	Take *it* off
P2	Look for *them*	Ø	I fell over	G	Give up *smoking*

Angus took the letter from his pocket and read it again by the light of the fire.

'I'd **tear** that **up** if I were you,' advised Ewan, 'and burn it. If the captain finds that on you, you'll **end up** being hanged as a rebel.'

'Aye,' replied Angus, throwing the pieces on to the fire. 'It's nearly dawn. I'll have to **take over** from the guard.'

'Well, take my advice and **wrap up** warmly. There'll be snow before morning.'

There were three men locked in the prison: Lord Lovat, Sir Duncan Fraser and Sir Donald Forbes. For many months they had been kept in close confinement with few comforts, so now it was difficult to **tell** one **from** another.

But at their first chance, their own people would try to overrun the castle and **let** them **out**.

Notes

tear up	N1 N2 P1	When you want to destroy something written, you can tear up the paper.
end up	Ø	If criminals are not careful they end up in prison. Many football matches end up as a draw.
take over	N1 N2 P1 Ø	Angus took over the work of the guard.
wrap up	N1 N2 P1 Ø	Before going out in the cold, it is a good idea to wrap up. You can also wrap up a parcel or a present.
let out	N1 N2 P1	A person who kept pets might let a cat out at night.
tell from	N1 P1	*See Unit 29*

Exercise A

Complete these sentences:

1 The Post Office has to advise people to . . . their parcels . . . well.
2 Argentina . . . . . . as World Champions in the 1986 World Cup Football Tournament.
3 My work was so bad that the teacher . . . it . . . in front of the whole class.
4 Tell me when you get tired and I'll . . . .
5 At the end of his sentence, the prison authorities . . . him . . . .
6 He took the wrong turning, got lost and . . . . in Birmingham.
7 The players were so covered with mud that you could not . . . one . . . another.
8 The dog wanted to go outside, so I . . . it . . . .

Exercise B

Answer these questions:

1 What do shop assistants do when you buy something delicate or fragile?
2 At what time are schoolchildren let out of school?
3 Would a Scot mistake one kind of whisky for another?
4 Who takes over when the president of a country is ill?
5 How could you make sure that nobody else read a private letter to you?
6 What could happen if you didn't pay your taxes?
7 If it were snowing what would you do before going out?
8 Name two things you would tear up.

N1	Take *your hat* off	N2	Look for *the keys*	P1	Take *it* off
P2	Look for *them*	Ø	I fell over	G	Give up *smoking*

The manager picked up the report his assistant had written and opened it.

'Frankly, Wilson, I'm not impressed. I've been **looking through** your report on the potential of the factory, and it leaves a lot to be desired. For example, you say that you think the mechanisation programme is satisfactory. I know we are advanced enough to **get by**, but I need to know where we succeed and where we fail. The design department can't **come up with** a solution to a problem if they don't know the problem. You **bring up** a few interesting ideas, but you **go on about** the siting of the factory for pages, as if there were anything we could do about it. And you seem to have **left out** altogether any mention of recreational facilities.

All in all, as a report, it's not much use to me at all.'

Notes

come up with	N2 P2	You can come up with a suggestion or an answer which is unexpected.
bring up	N1 N2 P1	You bring up a point for discussion if you raise it during a meeting.
go on about	N2 P2	If you liked talking about something, you might go on about it until somebody stopped you.
leave out	N1 N2 P1	If a point should have been included in a report, but was not, the writer left out that point.
look through	N2 P2	*See Unit 24*
get by	Ø	*See Unit 21*

Exercise A

Complete these sentences:

1 In the meeting, one of the committee members . . . . . . the problem of the size of the car park.
2 Fortunately somebody else . . . . a solution to the difficulty.
3 Can't you talk about something else? You always . . . . how unlucky you are.
4 I think that's all. Have I . . . anything . . .?
5 Nobody is going to give us any more money; we'll just have to . . . . . . on what we've got.
6 He . . . . how selfish we all were until we felt really miserable.
7 The bank has . . . . the idea of an extended loan, which suits us very well.
8 I'll . . . . . . your work and tell you what I think of it.

Exercise B

Answer these questions:

1 Name two things you could go on about.
2 What happens in a discussion?
3 Could you, given time, come up with a solution to every problem?
4 Does anyone look through your answers to these questions?
5 Can a country get by without oil?
6 Do you ever leave out an important point when you are writing a letter?
7 How often do you look through a foreign magazine?
8 Which countries have been left out of this list: Greece, West Germany, Britain, France, Belgium, Denmark, Luxembourg?

N1	Take *your hat* off	N2	Look for *the keys*	P1	Take *it* off
P2	Look for *them*	Ø	I fell over	G	Give up *smoking*

Michael:	Hello, John. Bad news, I'm afraid.
John:	What sort of bad news?
Michael:	It's about the play. Something's **come up** and I won't be able to act in the final performance.
John:	What? Oh no, that's all I need.
Michael:	My daughter's suddenly decided to get married that day.
John:	And can't she **put** it **off** for a few days?
Michael:	Not really. You see her husband's . . .
John:	I never thought I'd **run into** so many problems. First, my leading actress breaks her arm, then my leading actor says 'You'll have to **count** me **out**'. I'd better **call** the whole thing **off** before it's too late.
Michael:	You don't need to do that, and you know it. There are lots of people who could take the parts. Things will **turn out** all right, I'm sure.

Notes

put off	N1 N2 P1	You can put off an arrangement to a later time.
run into	N2 P2	You run into an unforeseen problem.
count out	N1 P1	You count a person out if you do not include her in an activity.
call off	N1 N2 P1	You call off an appointment, if you are unable to get to it and have to cancel it.
come up	Ø	*See Unit 22*
turn out	Ø	*See Unit 26*

Exercise A

Complete these sentences:

1 It looks as though there will be too much rain for the match; we'll have to . . . it . . . .
2 We were late arriving home because we . . . . . . a snowstorm.
3 The party . . . . to be a great success.
4 Apparently, some unforeseen problems have . . . ., and they will have to work all night.
5 Julie was expecting a baby so they had to . . . their holiday . . ..
6 James said they would have to . . . him . . . as he was not able to get a day off.
7 I really wish this problem hadn't . . . . at a time when I'm really busy.
8 I haven't got any more money to invest: you'll have to . . . me . . . .

Exercise B

Answer these questions:

1 What would a chairman of a meeting do if he felt ill just before the meeting?
2 What sort of difficulties come up while you are learning English?
3 What sort of problems do athletes run into?
4 Did your last examination results turn out as you had expected?
5 What would happen to an outdoor party if rain was expected?
6 What would a football team manager do if one of his players twisted an ankle before an important match?
7 What would happen to your flight if there was a strike at the airport?
8 What would happen to a party if none of the guests were able to come?

N1	Take *your hat* off	N2	Look for *the keys*
P2	Look for *them*	Ø	I fell over

P1	Take *it* off
G	Give up *smoking*

The debate was due to begin at 7.30, and by 7.15 the street outside the hall was so full that nobody could move. At length the doors opened and the audience rushed into the building.

Sir Edward let them **settle down**, and then introduced Mr Harold Eltonby, who was going to support the motion, proposing that the new steam railway should not be allowed to run through Cardenby. Unfortunately nobody had **turned up** to **speak for** the railway company, so the meeting looked as though it was going to be rather a disappointment.

Eltonby's speech **started off** with a virulent attack on modern morals and the evils of industrialisation. Before long, Sir Edward was **thinking about** something completely different and hoping that the meeting would soon **be over**.

Notes

settle down	Ø	At a concert, the musicians do not start playing until the audience has settled down.
start off	Ø	Speeches usually start off with an introduction. A film starts off with the titles.
think about	N2 P2	You think about something or somebody.
be over	Ø	The guests go home when a party is over.
turn up	Ø	*See Unit 23*
speak for	N2 P2	*See Unit 24*

Exercise A

Complete these sentences:

1 James isn't here – he always . . . . . . late.
2 Your proposal needs careful consideration. We'd like to . . . . . . it for a while.
3 Though the match . . . . . . in fine weather, it finished in rain.
4 The concert started as soon as the audience had . . . .
5 'I don't claim to . . . . . . everyone, but I hope I represent the views of the majority.'
6 The play finished in confusion, many of the audience leaving before it . . . .
7 He . . . . . . as a bank-clerk, but became a major financier.
8 Look who's . . . .! It's Joe. I thought you weren't coming.

Exercise B

Answer these questions:

1 Could you speak for yourself?
2 When would you leave a restaurant?
3 If you had an appointment at 6.30 a.m. would you turn up on time?
4 If you were offered a trip in a submarine what would you do?
5 Did your town start off as a village?
6 What would you do before watching a long film?
7 What will you do when this lesson is over?
8 What do you think about before going to sleep?

N1	Take *your hat* off	N2	Look for *the keys*	P1	Take *it* off
P2	Look for *them*	Ø	I fell over	G	Give up *smoking*

On Friday we got the keys to the house from the solicitor. We had intended to **move in** during the weekend, and had decided to **look in** and make sure that everything was all right.

As soon as we opened the door, I had the feeling that something was wrong. The air smelt too fresh for a house that had been locked and empty for three months. John had his bicycle lamp and I told him to **switch** it **on** – we knew the electricity had been **cut off** when the previous occupants left.

A window was smashed in the kitchen, there was rubbish everywhere, and all the curtains and carpets had been stolen. 'It's obvious someone has **broken in**,' I said. 'Let's **send for** the police.'

Notes

look in	Ø	The people looked in to check that everything was all right. Some
look in at	N2	people look in at a bar or a pub on their way home from work.
switch on	N1 N2 P1	You switch on a light, a television or an electric fire.
break in	Ø	An intruder had broken in. He had broken into the house.
break into	N2 P2	
send for	N2 P2	If there is an accident, you send for an ambulance.
move in	Ø	*See Unit 25*
cut off	N1 N2 P1	*See Unit 25*

Exercise A

Complete these sentences:

1 . . . the light . . ., would you? I can't see what I'm doing.
2 We'll . . . . . . when the decorators have finished.
3 During the night somebody . . . . . . and tried to open the safe.
4 We . . . . . . a taxi to take us to the theatre.
5 If you don't pay your electricity bill, they'll . . . you . . . .
6 Hello, Elena. I thought I'd . . . . . . and see how you are.
7 I had to . . . . . . because I've lost my key.
8 You'd better . . . . . . an ambulance; he looks quite badly hurt.

Exercise B

Answer these questions:

1 How can you get a taxi outside your front door?
2 Name four things you could switch on.
3 Do people ever look in to see if you are at home?
4 When did you move into your present home?
5 What would happen if you did not pay your telephone bill?
6 What do burglars do?
7 What would you do if you heard that a friend of yours was in hospital?
8 Has anyone ever broken into your home?

N1	Take *your hat* off	N2	Look for *the keys*	P1	Take *it* off
P2	Look for *them*	Ø	I fell over	G	Give up *smoking*

'I hope you will **take care of** the manuscript, Miss Grey,' said the priest. 'It is over five hundred years old.'

'I will, father,' replied Shirley.

He left her alone in the study as she **turned over** the vellum pages, reading the faded handwriting of some monk or priest who had died before Columbus sailed to America.

At the bottom of a page she **picked out** a detail that made her eyes **light up**. She **read** it **out**, almost unable to believe her voice: 'Sir Antony Gray, of Huntrington Manor, executed, July 20, 1415.' Sir Antony Gray had been executed, though all the other records said that he had been killed in battle. This **opened up** a world of possibilities that had never occurred to her.

Notes

turn over	N1 N2 P1 Ø	You turn over a page to the next when you come to the end of it.
light up	N1 N2 P1 Ø	The woman's eyes lit up because she was excited. You can also light up a cigarette.
read out	N1 N2 P1	When you say the words as you read you are reading something out.
open up	N1 N2 P1 Ø	The invention of aeroplanes opened up new possibilities for travel. The Suez Canal opened up the Middle East for trade and commerce. At the beginning of the day shops open up.
take care of	N2 P2	*See Unit 27*
pick out	N1 N2 P1	*See Unit 29*

Exercise A

Complete these sentences:

1 A face like his is not easy to . . . . . . in a crowd.
2 The inspector . . . . . . a list of men to be brought to the police station for questioning.
3 His discoveries . . . . . . a field of study that nobody had ever considered.
4 The pianist nodded and his assistant . . . the page . . . .
5 You may borrow my violin but please . . . . it.
6 His face . . . . . . when he heard the good news.
7 The question sheets were upside down on the desks: the students were told not to . . . them . . . until the exam began.
8 At the end of the meal, cigars were distributed and we all . . . .

Exercise B

Answer these questions:

1 If someone lent you a musical instrument, how would you treat it?
2 What would your face do if you heard some very good news?
3 What will you do when you come to the end of this page?
4 What did Vasco da Gama do?
5 What would you read out?
6 When do the police use an identity parade?
7 When you go to the butcher's, can you pick out the piece of meat you want to buy?
8 What happens at the beginning of committee meetings?

N1	Take *your hat* off	N2	Look for *the keys*	P1	Take *it* off
P2	Look for *them*	Ø	I fell over	G	Give up *smoking*

UNIT 40 *Saturn and Mars*

By the end of the year 2941, the Martian inter-galactic starships had almost completely blockaded the industrial southern hemisphere of Saturn. Saturnine trade was in direct competition with Mars, and the Martian rulers had decided they would **stand for** it no longer. In despair, the Saturnine Council **turned to** the Plutonian Master for help, but help arrived in a very different form. A Venusian peaceship, returning from deep space after gathering lost nuclear missiles for safe burial on Earth, landed on the agricultural side of Saturn to **stock up with** fresh food. This was the **breakthrough** the Saturnines needed. They announced to the Martians that they were holding the weapons; the Martians **called off** the blockade and **gave up** trying to enforce their will over the Saturnines.

Notes

stand for	N2	P2	*See Unit 24*
turn to	N2	P2	*See Unit 28*
stock up with	N2	P2	*See Unit 29*
break through	N2	P2	*See Unit 31*
call off	N1	N2 P1	*See Unit 36*
give up	N1	N2 P1 G	*See Unit 26*

Exercise A

Complete these sentences:

1 When the company was threatened with closure, we . . . . . . the Government for help.
2 Only two tickets for the performance were sold, so the management . . . it . . . .
3 I had to . . . . . . athletics so I could concentrate on getting my degree.
4 The tanks . . . . . . the line of foot soldiers.
5 Many people . . . . alcohol and cigarettes before the budget increases came into effect.
6 The police will not . . . . . . people taking the law into their own hands.
7 Surprisingly enough, I found it quite easy to . . . . . . smoking.
8 If there's one thing I won't . . . ., it's being treated like an idiot!

Exercise B

Answer these questions:

1 If you did not have time to study English, what would you do?
2 Who would you turn to if you needed advice on a point of law?
3 What do you consider to be the most important medical breakthrough this century?
4 What kind of food would you stock up with before a holiday?
5 Name three things your country's Government would not stand for.
6 What would happen if all the competitors in a race felt ill?
7 Do people ever turn to you for help?
8 Has any athlete ever broken through the barrier of 100 metres in 10 seconds?

N1	Take *your hat* off	N2	Look for *the keys*	P1	Take *it* off
P2	Look for *them*	Ø	I fell over	G	Give up *smoking*

Paul jumped on to the ledge and leant over the cashier's glass barrier.

'**Hand over** all the money in the till!' he shouted, waving his gun.

'You'll never **get away with** this,' said the cashier.

'**Look out for** cameras, Paul,' cried Andrew from the other side of the bank. 'We don't want our faces in every newspaper in the country. Right, that should **go off** in about thirty seconds.' Andrew had lit a gelignite charge next to the main safe. Neither of the robbers knew that there was a direct alarm from the bank to the police station; the police **were after** them at this very moment. In a few minutes the police would be **calling on** them to surrender. But there was a million dollars in the safe . . .

Notes

hand over	N1 N2 P1	The bank-robber wanted the cashier to hand the money over.
go off	Ø	A bomb or a firework goes off when it explodes. An alarm goes off when it starts to ring.
be after	N2 P2	The robbers were after the money, and the police were after them.
call on	N2 P2	You call on someone to do something like make a speech if you formally ask them to do it.
get away with	N2 P2 G	*See Unit 28*
look out for	N2 P2	*See Unit 29*

Exercise A

Complete these sentences:

1 The President . . . . . . the army to remain loyal.
2 Quick! The police . . . . . . us!
3 The soldiers . . . . . . their prisoner to the guards.
4 . . . . my brother while you are in London – he's working at Harrods.
5 The fireworks started to . . . . . . at half past nine.
6 Don't expect to . . . . not paying your taxes.
7 That's my watch, isn't it? . . . it . . ., you thief.
8 The terrorist threw a grenade but it . . . . . . without hurting anyone.

Exercise B

Answer these questions:

1 What would you look out for while walking in the countryside?
2 What happens when someone is caught with stolen goods?
3 What happens when a bomb hits the ground?
4 Are you ever called on to speak at meetings?
5 Do many people get away with shoplifting?
6 How would you know if the police were after a criminal?
7 What do opposition parties call on governments to do?
8 What would you do at the sales?

N1	Take *your hat* off	N2	Look for *the keys*	P1	Take *it* off
P2	Look for *them*	Ø	I fell over	G	Give up *smoking*

'Many people come to me and say "I **believe in** God". I usually say that I am glad, or "Praise the Lord" or something similar, and then I ask them if they really understand what is meant by giving your life to God. I explain that it means not only that you know that you can **count on** God, but also that he can **count on** you.

'I don't know why, but that **puts off** a lot of people. They say they'd like to **think** it **over**. Many of them try to make a bargain with God. Many of them **go through** the most awful torments of the soul. And some of them **end up** knowing that they must live their lives in the way God wants them to.'

Notes

believe in	N2 P2	You believe in God, or believe in a cause.
count on	N2 P2	You count on someone, if he is always reliable.
put off	N1 N2 P1	Something you do not like may put you off.
think over	N1 N2 P1	You think over a proposition that you are not sure about.
go through	N2 P2	*See Unit 33*
end up	Ø	*See Unit 34*

Exercise A

Complete these sentences:

1 Your proposal sounds quite interesting; I'd like to . . . it . . ..
2 It's just as I thought; I knew it would . . . . . . like this.
3 The thought of having to be vaccinated . . . her . . . the idea of a holiday in Morocco.
4 He's really reliable – you always . . . . . . him to do it right.
5 To be successful, a salesman has to . . . . . . what he is selling.
6 She . . . . . . a bad time when her husband left and she had to sell the house.
7 After years of dedicated work for the company, she . . . . . . being appointed as one of the directors.
8 People have always . . . . . . a deity or a being greater than themselves.

Exercise B

Answer these questions:

1 If someone offered you the post of Prime Minister would you accept it immediately?
2 Do many people believe in God?
3 Can you count on the weather to stay fine in summer?
4 Would having to work long hours put you off working in a theatre?
5 Do you go through a lot of pain if you burn your hand?
6 How did the American War of Independence end up?
7 Can you count on your car to start first time in cold weather?
8 What would you do before taking an important decision?

N1	Take *your hat* off	N2	Look for *the keys*	P1	Take *it* off
P2	Look for *them*	Ø	I fell over	G	Give up *smoking*

Dear Mum,

Just to let you know that everything is fine and the new job is all right.

The family I am working for are very pleasant, and you'd like them very much. They seem to think I have **settled down** to the American way of life very quickly, but I think it is very much like home. My work is to **tidy up** around the house, **put things away** and **dry up** after meals.

They have two little girls, aged 2 and 5, who seem to like me a lot. They are very well behaved, and I have only had to **tell** them **off** once so far. They like me to **tuck** them **in** when they go to bed.

I must go now as it is tea time.

Love, Frances.

Notes

put away	N1 N2 P1	To make a room tidy you can put things away in a cupboard.
dry up	Ø	When you have just washed up, you dry up.
tell off	N1 N2 P1	You might tell children off when they have been naughty.
tuck in	N1 N2 P1	When a child goes to bed, his mother might tuck him in.
settle down	Ø	*See Unit 37*
tidy up	N1 N2 P1 Ø	*See Unit 27*

Exercise A

Complete these sentences:

1 When you have finished with the iron could you . . . it . . . .
2 Teachers sometimes have to . . . children . . . .
3 If you wash up, I'll . . . .
4 February is a good time to . . . the garden . . . .
5 After three years' travelling abroad, he decided to get married and . . . .
6 The children liked to be . . . . at bedtime.
7 On 7 January we . . . the Christmas decorations . . . .
8 I gather he is beginning to . . . . . . now that he has a steady job.

Exercise B

Answer these questions:

1 When would you tell a child off?
2 What do some children like at bedtime?
3 What do you do when the dishes are wet?
4 At the beginning of a lesson what does a class do?
5 What would you do if there was a mess in your room?
6 Name two things you would put away after using them.
7 Have you ever been told off by the police?
8 How would you tidy up after a party?

N1	Take *your hat* off	N2	Look for *the keys*	P1	Take *it* off
P2	Look for *them*	Ø	I fell over	G	Give up *smoking*

Quentin was beginning to find the tension unbearable. He and the knight in black armour had been **drawn up** on opposite sides of the field and were to fight with axes for a purse of gold.

'I am sorry, my lord,' announced Quentin's page. 'The contest has been **held up** because of the arrival of Lady Alicia.' 'Well, tell the Master of Ceremonies that we want to **get on with** the fight. I've waited long enough.'

The page left. Quentin was beginning to feel uncomfortable: his armour was hot, and his helmet was tight and its padding thin.

'I wish I'd **tried on** that other helmet,' he thought. 'It was bigger and better padded. If I **fall over** in this I'll probably **knock** myself **out**.'

Notes

draw up	N1 N2 P1	The two knights were drawn up in their positions, facing each other.
hold up	N1 N2 P1	A delay held the contest up.
try on	N1 N2 P1	You try on clothes before you buy them.
fall over	Ø	If something loses its balance, it falls over.
knock out	N1 N2 P1	A heavy blow, especially on the head, might knock you out. If something knocks you out you lose consciousness.
get on with	N2 P2	*See Unit 31*

Exercise A

Complete these sentences:

1 Can I . . . that coat . . .? It looks my size.
2 Young children often . . . . . . when they are learning to walk.
3 A piece of falling plaster hit him on the head and . . . him . . . .
4 The captain . . . the soldiers . . . in a line and checked their weapons.
5 I find it very difficult to . . . . my work when the television is on.
6 The heavy snow . . . the trains . . . for a few hours.
7 The vase . . . . when he slammed the door.
8 The opposing armies were . . . . . . on either side of the valley.

Exercise B

Answer these questions:

1 What happens when someone loses his balance?
2 What would happen if someone hit you with a chair?
3 What do people do in clothes shops?
4 What happens if there is a delay?
5 Name two articles of clothing you would not try on before buying.
6 Where can you see soldiers drawn up on parade?
7 What happens in an office after the lunch break?
8 What happens if a tree falls on a railway line?

N1	Take *your hat* off	N2	Look for *the keys*	P1	Take *it* off
P2	Look for *them*	Ø	I fell over	G	Give up *smoking*

Steven:	John, look at this competition in the paper.
John:	A thousand pounds for the first correct answer. Come on, the paper's only just **come out**.
Steven:	O.K. **Write down** today's date, and multiply it by the year in which the Eiffel Tower was built.
John:	Um. 1885, I think.
Steven:	**Look** it **up**. There's an encyclopedia over there.
John:	1889. Built by Alexandre Gustave Eiffel (q.v.). What does q.v. **stand for**?
Steven:	*Quod vide.* It means there's an article about him in the encyclopedia as well. 1889 times today's date gives . . .
John:	24,522,998.
Steven:	Divided by 2 is 12,261,499.
John:	O.K. **Fill in** your name and address and I'll **tear** this piece of paper **up**.
Steven:	Why?
John:	So that nobody else can use our calculations, of course.

Notes

write down	N1 N2 P1	You write something down on paper.
look up	N1 N2 P1	You look up information in a reference book.
stand for	N2 P2	In an abbreviation, the initials stand for the full name of what is being indicated e.g. U.K. stands for United Kingdom.
fill in	N1 N2 P1	When you fill in a form, you fill your name in.
come out	Ø	*See Unit 32*
tear up	N1 N2 P1	*See Unit 34*

Exercise A

Complete these sentences:

1 He . . . the letter . . . so that nobody should read it.
2 We had to . . . . . . a lot of forms before we could get our visas for Russia.
3 I'd better . . . your telephone number . . . or I'll forget it.
4 He bought a copy of the new book the day it . . . .
5 I did not know what the word meant so I . . . it . . . in the dictionary.
6 You've never told us your full name – I know it's Eric R. Forton, but what does the 'R' . . . . ..?
7 The report was so inaccurate that I . . . it . . ..
8 Could you . . . . the times of the trains to Exmouth?

Exercise B

Answer these questions:

1 What do you do with a form?
2 What do your initials stand for?
3 How often do daily papers come out?
4 Do you write down the answers to these questions?
5 Have you ever torn a bank note up by mistake?
6 How can you find out who the tenth Roman emperor was?
7 What would you do if you wanted to remember someone's telephone number?
8 What do you do when you travel to a foreign country by plane?

N1 Take *your hat* off	N2 Look for *the keys*	P1 Take *it* off
P2 Look for *them*	Ø I fell over	G Give up *smoking*

UNIT 46   *An Interview with a Sportsman*

'Were you young when you **took up** archery?' asked the interviewer.

'No, not at all,' replied Daniel. 'You see, I was born and **brought up** in a part of Manchester where people probably would not have known what archery was if you had asked them. I began at University when I was nineteen. In fact, I **started off** with a wooden bow, with wooden arrows to **go with** it.'

'And did you win many prizes at University?'

'No. My first bow was awful, and, in fact, I **gave** it **back** to the shop. I had to borrow one until I had **saved up** enough to buy a decent composite bow. And I think I won my first competition a month later.'

Notes

take up	N1 N2 P1 G	You take up a sport or hobby when you start doing it regularly.
go with	N2 P2	Cups go with saucers. Knives go with forks.
give back	N1 N2 P1	You give back something you have borrowed.
save up	N1 N2 P1 Ø	If you wanted to buy a car, but did not have enough money, you would be able to afford it after you had saved up the money.
bring up	N1 N2 P1	*See Unit 35*
start off	Ø	*See Unit 37*

Exercise A

Complete these sentences:

1 We aren't going on holiday because we are . . . . . . to buy a car.
2 You should find a new interest; why don't you . . . . . . painting?
3 . . . . . . children requires a lot of responsibility.
4 The tour of Europe . . . . . . in Paris and ended in Athens.
5 They bought a set of plates and some bowls to . . . . . . them.
6 Can I borrow some money? I'll . . . it . . . next week.
7 The U.K. . . . . . . as four separate countries.
8 Deposit accounts can help you . . . . . . for a house, a car or a holiday abroad.

Exercise B

Answer these questions:

1 Which word goes with *up*: *off*, *out* or *down*?
2 When do you have to give back library books?
3 What would you save up for?
4 What do parents do?
5 Which sport would you like to take up?
6 If you wanted to learn how to ski, how would you start off?
7 What would you do if you borrowed someone's umbrella?
8 Why did you take up learning English?

N1	Take *your hat* off	N2	Look for *the keys*
P2	Look for *them*	Ø	I fell over

P1	Take *it* off
G	Give up *smoking*

'Mr Crick, the detective?' asked the butler.

'Indeed,' Crick replied. 'I presume you are the butler. Please, be good enough to **show** me **round**.'

'Certainly, sir,' said the butler, leading Crick into a large study. 'The thieves **broke in** through the window, sir.'

'Yesterday evening, I believe, at about this time?'

'Indeed, sir,' continued the butler. 'Mr Watson was out of the room between 6.30 and 7.00 p.m.'

'Do you mind if I **look over** the room?'

'Not at all, sir.'

Crick studied the broken window, the contents of Mr Watson's desk and a large African palm which had been left lying on its side.

He **took down** some notes on his pad.

'**Switch** the light **off**, would you? Thanks. Yes,' he said, 'I shall have to **think** this **over** very carefully.'

Notes

show round	N1 P1	You show someone round a house, taking him from room to room.
look over	N1 N2 P1 P2	You look over a room or a house if you want to inspect it before buying.
take down	N1 N2 P1	You take down notes during a lecture.
switch off	N1 N2 P1	You switch off a light, or a TV.
break in	Ø	*See Unit 38*
think over	N1 N2 P1	*See Unit 42*

Exercise A

Complete these sentences:

1 The proposal didn't seem a bad one once we'd . . . it . . . .
2 He . . . the light . . . and left the room.
3 This window is smashed. I hope nobody has . . . .
4 She . . . . her work to check that there were no mistakes.
5 You haven't seen the house; let me . . . you . . . .
6 I . . . . a few notes while the lecturer was speaking.
7 I've lost my keys, I think we'll have to . . . . . . the house.
8 We're going to Coventry to . . . . . . John's new factory.

Exercise B

Answer these questions:

1 What does a guide do?
2 What do students do during a lecture?
3 What do you do before going to sleep?
4 What would you do if you were offered a lot of money to do a dangerous job?
5 What do people do before buying a flat?
6 How would you know if someone had broken into your house?
7 What do newspaper reporters do during interviews?
8 What would you do after using an electric typewriter?

N1	Take *your hat* off	N2	Look for *the keys*	P1	Take *it* off
P2	Look for *them*	Ø	I fell over	G	Give up *smoking*

As the coach was making its way through the forest a figure wearing a dark cloak and mask and holding a loaded pistol appeared on the path. The coach stopped and the highwayman **got off** his horse. He opened the door of the coach and asked the passengers, an old gentleman and his daughter and two younger men, to come outside. '**Line up** beside the road and **put** your hands **up**,' he told them.
'I do not want your watches or jewellery, Sir George,' he said to the old man, 'You have with you a document I need.'
'The King's command for the arrest of Jack Tolby!'
'Jack Tolby, at your service,' the highwayman said, bowing. 'It is in the box under your seat, I think. **Hand over** the key.'
He took the key, and in an instant, he had **opened up** the box, taken the document, remounted his horse, wished the travellers a safe journey and **turned back** into the forest.

Notes

get off	N2 P2 Ø	You get off a bus, a bicycle or a train.
line up	Ø	People line up when they queue for something.
put up	N1 N2 P1	They put their hands up above their heads, so that he could see that they had no guns. Decorators put up wallpaper.
turn back	Ø	If you had driven down a road with no exit you would have to turn back.
hand over	N1 N2 P1	*See Unit 41*
open up	N1 N2 P1 Ø	*See Unit 39*

Exercise A

Complete these sentences:

1 When the fire-alarm went off, the children left their classrooms and . . . . . . on the field.
2 Two weeks before Christmas, we . . . . . . the Christmas decorations.
3 I . . . . . . the bus at Piccadilly and walked to the cinema.
4 The bank manager, who knew the combination of the lock, was ordered to . . . . . . the strong-room.
5 The snow was lying five feet deep in places, so we decided to . . . .
6 In the police station, the thief was made to . . . . . . everything in his pockets.
7 Ten people had . . . . . . to wait for the bus.
8 I had to . . . . . . when I got to the station as all the trains had been cancelled.

Exercise B

Answer these questions:

1 What would a soldier do when told to surrender?
2 What would you do if you had started a journey but were unable to continue?
3 What does a shopkeeper do early in the morning?
4 What do you do at the end of a train journey?
5 When would you see people lining up outside a shop?
6 What would a pickpocket do when taken to a police station?
7 When do schoolchildren put their hands up?
8 Name four things you can get off.

N1	Take *your hat* off	N2	Look for *the keys*	P1	Take *it* off
P2	Look for *them*	Ø	I fell over	G	Give up *smoking*

Mrs Perkins:	Are you still working? It's time you went to bed.
Alan:	But I've got to finish this essay.
Mrs Perkins:	Surely it's not that urgent. Can't you **put** it **off** till tomorrow?
Alan:	No. I've got to **hand** it **in** tomorrow. I've finished the preparation, and I'm halfway through writing it.
Mrs Perkins:	Well, go to bed when you've done that.
Alan:	I think it will be better if I **stay up** and do it all tonight. You see, I'll have to **write** it **out** again with the maps and diagrams. When I've **got through** that I'll go to bed.
Mrs Perkins:	Why did you stay out so long if you knew you had work to do? I wish you'd **think about** your work a bit more often.

Notes

hand in	N1 N2 P1	At the end of an examination you hand in your papers.
stay up	Ø	If you had to work all night to complete a job, you would have to stay up.
write out	N1 N2 P1	You can write out a report or a cheque. Alan planned his essay in note form, then he wrote it out in full.
get through	N2 P2	If you work until you finish doing something you get through it.
put off	N1 N2 P1	*See Unit 36*
think about	N2 P2	*See Unit 37*

Exercise A

Complete these sentences:

1 I'll be able to go out when I have . . . . . . this job.
2 Shall we . . . . and watch the late film on television?
3 Give me a couple of days to . . . . . . your suggestion and I'll let you know.
4 If it rains we shall . . . the match . . . till tomorrow.
5 She . . . . her application and posted it that afternoon.
6 As I was going near the office, I thought I could . . . the form . . . personally.
7 On Midsummer's Eve we . . . . to watch the sun rise.
8 I told him the main points, but he asked me to . . . them . . . so that he could study them himself.

Exercise B

Answer these questions:

1 What would you do if you wanted to see a late programme on TV?
2 How long does it take you to get through these exercises?
3 Do you write out your answers to these questions in a book?
4 What do you do at the end of a written examination?
5 What would you do if you had toothache on the day you had arranged to go out for dinner?
6 Do you think about what you are going to say before answering?
7 How often do people have to hand in their passports for renewal?
8 How long will it take you to get through the rest of this book?

N1	Take *your hat* off	N2	Look for *the keys*	P1	Take *it* off
P2	Look for *them*	Ø	I fell over	G	Give up *smoking*

'And now here are the news headlines again.

This afternoon a bomb **went off** in Brents department store. Nobody was injured, and so far nobody has claimed responsibility.

The Prime Minister has **called on** the Civil Service unions to cancel their proposed strike on Wednesday.

The Chancellor of the Exchequer, speaking to undergraduates of Cambridge University, has said that the majority of voters **believe in** the Government's current economic policy. The people of Britain could **count on** the Government to make Britain rich again, he said.

The Post Office is **putting up** the postage rates. From the end of next month a first class letter will cost three pence more and a second class letter two pence more.

And scientists have **come up with** evidence which proves that the Loch Ness Monster is nothing more than a family of otters.'

Notes

go off	Ø	*See Unit 41*
call on	N2 P2	*See Unit 41*
believe in	N2 P2	*See Unit 42*
count on	N2 P2	*See Unit 42*
put up	N1 N2 P1	*See Unit 48*
come up with	N2 P2	*See Unit 35*

Exercise A

Complete these sentences:

1 The research unit say they have . . . . some new ideas about cancer.
2 We knew we could . . . . . . you to arrive on time.
3 Do you think many people . . . . . . ghosts nowadays?
4 The captain . . . . . . the players to do their best.
5 The fire alarm . . . . . . because so many people were smoking.
6 We had to . . . . the cost of the paint because it was costing more to produce it.
7 I'm . . . . . . you; don't disappoint me.
8 The chairman . . . . . . me to thank Mr Wilkins for his work on the committee.

Exercise B

Answer these questions:

1 When did the Government last put up the cost of postage?
2 When will they come up with a solution to the world's energy shortage?
3 Do young children believe in Father Christmas?
4 Have you ever seen a bomb go off?
5 What do police call on criminals to do?
6 Can you count on public transport to get you somewhere on time?
7 What is an atheist?
8 What happens when petrol companies have to pay more for the petrol they sell?

N1 Take *your hat* off	N2 Look for *the keys*	P1 Take *it* off
P2 Look for *them*	Ø I fell over	G Give up *smoking*

In a corner of the luxurious room the lights **were on** above a card table with six men playing poker. A number of people were watching the game with interest.

A few minutes after Hugh had arrived, one of the men threw his cards on the table and said, 'You can **count** me **out**. I've nothing left to lose.'

Hugh said to the other players, 'Do you mind if I **join in**?'

A Spaniard with a silk waistcoat nodded, and Hugh sat down and **took off** his jacket.

After twenty minutes, ten thousand dollars had changed hands. The crowd watched, fascinated. One by one the players lost their money and **dropped out**, until only Hugh and the Spaniard were left. The game was **turning into** a duel between two men whose pockets seemed to have no bottom.

Notes

be on	Ø	When he came home the light was on, he had forgotten to switch it off. The news bulletin is on the radio at six o'clock.
take off	N1 N2 P1	You take your coat off if you are too hot.
turn into	N2 P2	If you freeze water it turns into ice. A demonstration can turn into a riot if it gets out of control.
count out	N1 P1	*See Unit 36*
join in	N2 Ø	*See Unit 32*
drop out	Ø	*See Unit 32*

Exercise A

Complete these sentences:

1 George is ill – we'll have to . . . him . . . .
2 You look feverish: . . . . . . those wet clothes and sit by the fire.
3 Unfortunately, thirteen people had been invited to dinner by mistake, so I offered to . . . .
4 The film . . . . . . at 8.30, so we'd better leave now.
5 As the wind grew stronger, the storm . . . . . . a tempest.
6 He listened to the conversation but didn't . . . .
7 It's terribly hot in here; . . . the fire . . .?
8 I was invited to . . . ., but I couldn't, as I was so busy.

Exercise B

Answer these questions:

1 Is the light on in this room?
2 What does water turn into if you boil it?
3 What do you do after coming in out of the rain?
4 What happens if a rider falls off his horse during a race?
5 What would happen to a student if he got very low marks?
6 Why did so many countries join in the fighting in World War I?
7 What do you do when the weather is hot?
8 In winemaking, what does sugar turn into?

N1 Take *your hat* off	N2 Look for *the keys*	P1 Take *it* off
P2 Look for *them*	Ø I fell over	G Give up *smoking*

UNIT 52 *A Problem on the Journey*

There were six of us going by car to Andrew's wedding. I decided to go with Paul and Susan but, a mile from Oxted, Paul noticed that there was steam coming from under the bonnet of our car. The other car stopped in front of us, and Eric came over and said, 'What's happened? Have you **broken down**?'
Susan was furious; she just sat there, **winding** her watch **up** and looking straight ahead.
'We're going to be late,' she said.
'Look, Eric,' I said, 'we've **run into** a bit of a problem. The radiator's boiling. Could you **get in touch with** Andrew and tell him we've been **held up**. We'll try and **catch** you **up** as soon as we can.'

Notes

break down	Ø	A car or any piece of machinery breaks down if it stops working.
wind up	N1 N2 P1	You need to wind up some types of watch every day.
get in touch with	N2 P2	You can get in touch with someone by writing to her or ringing her up.
run into	N2 P2	*See Unit 36*
hold up	N1 N2 P1	*See Unit 44*
catch up	N1 P1 Ø	*See Unit 33*

Exercise A

Complete these sentences:

1 You go on – we'll try to . . . you . . . later.
2 The clock has stopped. I suppose I must have forgotten to . . . it . . ..
3 He apologised for being late, and explained that he had . . . . . . a bit of trouble on the way.
4 I don't know what is wrong with this machine – it keeps . . . .
5 Right, I'll . . . . you when I get back from Sicily.
6 Traffic has been . . . . . . in central London due to a burst water main.
7 I think I'll have to work all night to . . . .
8 Nowadays, many watches are automatic or electric, so you don't have to . . . them . . ..

Exercise B

Answer these questions:

1 What do you have to do to a clock?
2 Were you held up on your way here?
3 How can you get in touch with a friend in another country?
4 What happens to a car if water gets in the motor?
5 What would a student do after missing a week of lessons?
6 What would you do if you ran into a problem?
7 Name four ways in which a car can break down.
8 What happens when the roads have to be repaired?

N1	Take *your hat* off	N2	Look for *the keys*	P1	Take *it* off
P2	Look for *them*	Ø	I fell over	G	Give up *smoking*

My Aunt Jane is fantastically rich but, as she isn't easy to **get on with**, she does not have many friends. I suppose that is why she **looks forward to** Christmas so much – because all the family write to her and she does not feel so lonely.

I **sent off** my Christmas cards a couple of weeks before Christmas and then went to stay with some friends in Ireland for the festive season. I don't know how on earth it **came about**, but somehow I **left** Aunt Jane **out** of my list of people to send Christmas cards to. The first I heard about it was a letter from Aunt Clarissa, thoroughly **telling** me **off** for being so thoughtless. I apologised to her and to Aunt Jane, but even so, I bet they've both revised their wills.

Notes

get on with	N2 P2	Aunt Jane did not have many friends. People did not find it easy to get on with her.
send off	N1 N2 P1	You send off a letter when you put it in the postbox.
come about	Ø	He could not see how he had made such a mistake – he did not know how it had come about.
look forward to	N2 P2 G	*See Unit 31*
leave out	N1 N2 P1	*See Unit 35*
tell off	N1 N2 P1	*See Unit 43*

Exercise A

Complete these sentences:

1 He wrote the letter and . . . it . . . immediately.
2 I . . . the dog . . . for barking at the children.
3 You've lost your job? How did that . . . . . .?
4 She was depressed because she had been . . . . . . of the team.
5 We're sorry you can't come, as we were . . . . seeing you.
6 I would say, even though she is my sister, that she is quite difficult to . . . .
7 I've . . . . my applications; now I'll just have to wait for the replies.
8 It's a complete mystery; nobody knows how it . . . . at all.

Exercise B

Answer these questions:

1 How would you deal with a naughty child?
2 How did your interest in English come about?
3 Do you get on with most of your friends?
4 England, Wales, Northern Ireland; which country has been left out?
5 Name two things you are looking forward to.
6 What do you do with letters?
7 Have you left out any of these questions?
8 Do you find British people easy to get on with?

N1	Take *your hat* off	N2	Look for *the keys*	P1	Take *it* off
P2	Look for *them*	Ø	I fell over	G	Give up *smoking*

When I met Robert he was rather depressed. He had just been **thrown out** of college for not working hard enough, and his plans for a holiday in Turkey had **fallen through** for lack of money.
I asked him what he intended to do.
'I'll get a job. **I'm after** a job I saw in the paper yesterday. Yes, I'm definitely going to **pull myself together** and get a job.'
It was easy to see that he had invented this story there and then.
I asked him if this was so.
'Yes,' he said, 'I have seen a few jobs in the papers, but I haven't **got round to** applying for them yet.'
I asked what he had done since leaving college.
'I've **taken up** chess. But I have to play against myself as there's no-one else at home.'

Notes

throw out	N1 N2 P1	The authorities had thrown Robert out of college for laziness.
fall through	Ø	Robert had planned to go to Turkey, but he was unable to go. His plans had fallen through.
be after	N2 P2	He was after a job he had seen in the paper. He wanted to get it.
get round to	N2 P2 G	When he stopped delaying it, he would get round to applying for a job.
pull yourself together	P1	*See Unit 33*
take up	N1 N2 P1 G	*See Unit 46*

Exercise A

Complete these sentences:

1 You will have to . . . yourself . . . if you want to win the game.
2 I have played golf once or twice, but I've never . . . it . . . seriously.
3 It looks as though the plans will . . . ., so we shall have to think of something else.
4 The tennis club committee . . . him . . ., because he had stolen some money from the bar.
5 I've saved some money and I . . . . . . a good second-hand camera.
6 I dare say she will . . . . signing the contract sooner or later.
7 They would like to . . . him . . . of the society, but he is the President's son.
8 If the weather gets better I might . . . . doing something in the garden.

Exercise B

Answer these questions:

1 What happens to people who fight in bars?
2 What sort of people go to antique markets?
3 What would you do if you couldn't concentrate on your work?
4 When did you take up learning English?
5 Does a lazy person do things at the earliest possible opportunity?
6 What would you do if your holiday plans fell through?
7 What would you do if someone else were after your job?
8 Have you ever considered taking up sport as a career?

N1	Take *your hat* off	N2	Look for *the keys*	P1	Take *it* off
P2	Look for *them*	Ø	I fell over	G	Give up *smoking*

UNIT 55 *A Phone Call*

Liza **turned on** the lights and closed the office door. She stood watching the fluorescent strip lights **light up**, one by one, and then walked to the window. Thomson had said he would **ring** her **back** to let her know which way the committee voted, for or against her proposals for closing the power stations.

The telephone rang. Thomson spoke.

'Thomson here. I don't think you have many friends on the committee. They don't like you very much.'

'Well, frankly, I don't **get on** very well **with** them. But that's not why you phoned. Which way did they vote?'

'They haven't voted yet. There was a delay.'

'Oh, yes. And how did that **come about**?'

'Well, I don't know how to put this. To be honest, one of the committee members **put forward** a suggestion that you should resign as president of the company.'

Notes

turn on	N1 N2 P1	You can turn on the lights, the fire or the TV.
light up	N1 N2 P1 Ø	The lights lit up the room, which had previously been in the dark.
ring back	N1 N2 P1 Ø	You can ring somebody back after a first phone call.
put forward	N1 N2 P1	You can put forward a suggestion or a proposal.
get on with	N2 P2	*See Unit 53*
come about	Ø	*See Unit 53*

Exercise A

Complete these sentences:

1 We did not know what to do until James . . . . . . the idea of going for a picnic.
2 The floodlights . . . . . . the whole of the stadium.
3 . . . the television . . ., would you? I want to see the news.
4 I like Jane very much, but I just can't . . . . her parents.
5 I don't know how it . . . . . ., but nothing was prepared for after the wedding.
6 O.K., I'll . . . you . . . as soon as I get the news.
7 That's a stupid explanation. Who . . . it . . .?
8 Many religious sects have predicted the end of the world, but they are reluctant to say when this will . . . .

Exercise B

Answer these questions:

1 What do you do when you get up in the morning?
2 What are spotlights in a theatre for?
3 Name one person you get on with well.
4 When would you ring someone back?
5 Who first put forward the idea of gravity?
6 How do you think the beginning of the world came about?
7 Name four things you could turn on.
8 What happens when you press a light switch?

N1	Take *your hat* off	N2	Look for *the keys*	P1	Take *it* off
P2	Look for *them*	Ø	I fell over	G	Give up *smoking*

Frances:	Hello Marion.
Assistant:	Hello Mrs Jackson. How are you?
Frances:	Fine thanks. That's a nice jacket.
Assistant:	Yes, it only arrived yesterday. Italian silk. I think it's your size.
Frances:	It would **go** nicely **with** my white skirt, don't you think?
Assistant:	Well, **take off** your jacket and **try it on**.
Frances:	Oh, it's lovely. And it fits perfectly.
Assistant:	Yes, it suits you very well.
Frances:	How much is it?
Assistant:	Forty-eight pounds.
Frances:	Good. **Wrap** it **up** for me, would you. Now I can **throw out** that terrible pink jacket George's aunt made for me.
Assistant:	There you are, Mrs Jackson. Thank you for **looking in**.
Frances:	Bye-bye Marion. And thank you.

Notes

go with	N2 P2	Black shoes go with a blue suit.
take off	N1 N2 P1	*See Unit 51*
try on	N1 N2 P1	*See Unit 44*
wrap up	N1 N2 P1 Ø	*See Unit 34*
throw out	N1 N2 P1	*See Unit 54*
look in	Ø	*See Unit 38*

Exercise A

Complete these sentences:

1 If you're not in a hurry, ... on your way back from the hospital.
2 The pilot . . . . . . his earphones and left the cabin.
3 I'll . . . . . . the books for you so that they don't get wet.
4 These trousers are too tight for me. Could I . . . . . . a larger pair?
5 We bought a teapot and a coffeepot to . . . . . . our new dinner service.
6 I don't think these shoes can be repaired again; I'd better . . . them . . . .
7 He undid his coat and . . . it . . . .
8 If anybody wants any furniture, we're going to . . . . . . a lot of ours.

Exercise B

Answer these questions:

1 Name two things you could wrap up.
2 Which colour goes well with yellow?
3 What would you do with a broken washing-machine that could not be repaired?
4 Would you try a shirt on before buying it?
5 What would you do before going indoors, if your shoes were muddy?
6 Do you look in at any shops on your way home?
7 Give the names of two kinds of food which go well with each other e.g. fish and white sauce.
8 Where would you go if you wanted to try on a suit of armour?

N1	Take *your hat* off	N2	Look for *the keys*	P1	Take *it* off
P2	Look for *them*	Ø	I fell over	G	Give up *smoking*

'I must say,' said Peter, 'I didn't like the way old Watkins **dealt with** Cynthia this morning.'

'Watkins, the production supervisor?' I asked.

'That's him. Cynthia's the girl who does most of his typing.'

'What happened?'

'Well, you know what he's like,' said Peter. 'He gets quite angry when things don't run smoothly, and that **puts** a lot of people **off**. I know Cynthia's had some time off for sickness . . .'

'Yes,' I interrupted, 'isn't she the one who was off for two weeks with a cold?'

'That's her. Anyway, Watkins **sent for** her this morning, and by the time she arrived he looked as if he was **turning into** some kind of animal. He started shouting and she just **broke down** and started crying.'

'What did he do?' I asked.

'Just sent her home to **get over** it.'

Notes

break down	Ø	If a person is very upset or under great strain, he or she could break down.
deal with	N2 P2	*See Unit 15*
put off	N1 N2 P1	*See Unit 42*
send for	N2 P2	*See Unit 38*
turn into	N2 P2	*See Unit 51*
get over	N2 P2	*See Unit 26*

Exercise A

Complete these sentences:

1 When the lawyer started to ask very personal questions, the witness . . . . . . and wept.

2 Never mind. You'll . . . . . . it and then you'll be all right.

3 I wonder who could . . . . . . your problem; I don't think I can.

4 . . . . . . the police! There's been a burglary.

5 He appears, at first, to be very arrogant, which . . . a lot of people . . . .

6 Slowly, the chemicals in the bottle began to . . . . . . a heavy gas.

7 We don't have the facilities for . . . . . . this kind of emergency.

8 It's a very nice cafe, but the smell of smoke . . . me . . . .

Exercise B

Answer these questions:

1 What do magic spells do?

2 How would you send for a taxi?

3 Does the smell of petrol fumes put you off?

4 What happens to people when they are under too much pressure?

5 What does soil turn into when it rains?

6 How long does it take a person to get over a broken arm?

7 Whose job is it to deal with traffic jams?

8 If someone was suddenly taken ill, what would you do?

N1	Take *your hat* off	N2	Look for *the keys*	P1	Take *it* off
P2	Look for *them*	Ø	I fell over	G	Give up *smoking*

The professor **read out** the examination instructions and then told the students to **turn over** the question papers on their desks. Carol **wrote down** some notes while she was listening.

There were three questions she could answer, though she knew that the views she would **put forward** would definitely conflict with those of the professor.

'Very well,' she thought, 'I must compromise. I'll answer the first question in my way, and when I've **got through** that, I'll answer the other two in a way the professor will like. That way, he'll know I could have done the whole paper presenting my views, but that I wanted to pass the exam.'

At the end of two hours she **handed in** her script. She would have to wait two days to hear the results.

Notes

read out	N1 N2 P1	*See Unit 39*
turn over	N1 N2 P1 Ø	*See Unit 39*
write down	N1 N2 P1	*See Unit 45*
put forward	N1 N2 P1	*See Unit 55*
get through	N2 P2	*See Unit 49*
hand in	N1 N2 P1	*See Unit 49*

Exercise A

Complete these sentences:

1 You are late. You should have . . . your work . . . yesterday.
2 The teacher . . . . . . the dates of the examinations so that everyone could read them.
3 She . . . the parcel . . . and wrote her own address on the other side.
4 During the service, the priest . . . . . . the names of the people who wanted to get married.
5 I'd like to . . . . . . this job while there is still enough sunlight.
6 It is a good suggestion and I am glad you . . . it . . . .
7 The judge . . . . . . the list of crimes she was supposed to have committed.
8 Hold on. I'll get a pencil and . . . it . . . .

Exercise B

Answer these questions:

1 When will you get through this book?
2 What do you do after completing some written work?
3 What do politicians put forward in Parliament?
4 What do you do when you finish reading the first page of a book?
5 What happens after the votes have been counted in an election?
6 Why do people keep address books?
7 Do you get through more work in the mornings or the afternoons?
8 What do you do after grilling one side of a steak?

N1	Take *your hat* off	N2	Look for *the keys*	P1	Take *it* off
P2	Look for *them*	Ø	I fell over	G	Give up *smoking*

'So this will be your first home?' asked the agent.

Jack said 'yes' and Sylvia said 'no' at the same time. Jack explained. 'We had been **saving up** to buy a house, but it all **fell through** because I lost my job.'

'I see,' said the agent. 'Well, I can **show** you **round** some decent flats.'

'Good,' replied Sylvia. 'What's the procedure?'

'Every week we print a list of the flats we have for sale. Here's this week's. I want you to **take** it **away** and give it a good **look over**. And then let me know which ones you like.'

'Do you want me to pay a deposit now?' asked Jack.

'Oh, don't worry about that now. We'll **get round to** that sort of thing later.'

Notes

save up	N1 N2 P1 Ø	*See Unit 46*
fall through	Ø	*See Unit 54*
show round	N1 P1	*See Unit 47*
take away	N1 N2 P1	*See Unit 28*
look over	N1 N2 P1 P2	*See Unit 47*
get round to	N2 P2 G	*See Unit 54*

Exercise A

Complete these sentences:

1 The guards . . . the prisoner . . . for questioning.
2 I'm going to buy a car; I've been . . . . . . for months.
3 We have a possibility of a holiday in Sri Lanka, but if that . . . . . . we shall go down to the cottage.
4 They had so much work to do that they did not know when they would . . . . reading my manuscript.
5 We decided to . . . . . . the factory building to see if it would be suitable.
6 Come on. I'll . . . you . . . the estate.
7 I haven't marked your essay yet, but I should . . . . it next week.
8 We haven't got the contract. The whole deal has . . . .

Exercise B

Answer these questions:

1 Could you buy a new car now?
2 What would you do if a friend visited you at your new home?
3 What does a waiter do at the end of a meal?
4 When will you get round to reading this book again?
5 What would you do before buying a bicycle?
6 What would you do if your plans to work abroad fell through?
7 How long would it take you to save up to buy a yacht?
8 Do you have to stay in a library when you read library books?

N1	Take *your hat* off	N2	Look for *the keys*	P1	Take *it* off
P2	Look for *them*	Ø	I fell over	G	Give up *smoking*

'Good morning, Janet.'

'Hello, Mrs Felton.'

'I have to go out this morning, Janet. But there are a lot of things I want you to do. You'd better get your pad and **take down** the list of jobs.

First, could you **put** all these files **away**; I should have done it myself but I haven't had time. Next I want you to **get in touch with** Dawlish & Co. and tell them that we haven't received the forms we ordered last month. Then I want you to **send** these letters **off**, first class. Now, I have these notes about the board meeting yesterday. Could you **write** them **out** so that they make good sense, and send them downstairs to be typed. I think that's all. No, just one more thing. Can you **look up** the times of trains to Plymouth on Friday.'

Notes

take down	N1 N2 P1	*See Unit 47*
put away	N1 N2 P1	*See Unit 43*
get in touch with	N2 P2	*See Unit 52*
send off	N1 N2 P1	*See Unit 53*
write out	N1 N2 P1	*See Unit 49*
look up	N1 N2 P1	*See Unit 45*

Exercise A

Complete these sentences:

1 On the Saturday before Christmas I wrote eighteen letters and . . . them . . . .

2 The reporters . . . . . . every word the Minister said.

3 I'll . . . the report . . . tonight and give it to you tomorrow.

4 It's a terribly difficult passage. I had to . . . . . . half the words to find out what they meant.

5 At the end of the lesson we . . . our books . . . and left the room.

6 Could you . . . . me as soon as you have the examination results.

7 She . . . . . . a cheque and gave it to the shop assistant.

8 I must remind you that every word you say will be . . . . . . and may be used in evidence against you.

Exercise B

Answer these questions:

1 What does a clerk in a court of law do?

2 When do people send off a lot of parcels and letters?

3 Name three things you could write out.

4 How could you find out the meaning of a word you did not know?

5 What do you do with the clean plates after a meal?

6 How can we get in touch with someone in space?

7 What is a telephone directory for?

8 Would you put a record-player away after using it?

N1	Take *your hat* off	N2	Look for *the keys*	P1	Take *it* off
P2	Look for *them*	Ø	I fell over	G	Give up *smoking*

Combine each of the following pairs of verbs in one sentence.

1	build up, take off.	29	decide on, ring up.
2	go ahead, try on.	30	write out, throw away.
3	ring back, find out.	31	fill in, send off.
4	come up, deal with.	32	turn out, go with.
5	give up, drop out.	33	think about, fit in with.
6	dry up, put away.	34	wake up to, be after.
7	drop in, pick up.	35	go on about, cut off from.
8	go through, look for.	36	look in, be on.
9	put forward, do without.	37	call on, turn down.
10	run over, wait for.	38	stock up with, run out of.
11	wake up, pour in.	39	pick up, write down.
12	cut off, call back.	40	pull yourself together, face up to.
13	count on, get rid of.	41	look after, grow up.
14	wrap up, take away.	42	come up with, sort out.
15	go through, cope with.	43	make up, mistake for.
16	stay up, work out.	44	get on with, clear up.
17	open up, let out.	45	count out, fall through.
18	break in, get away with.	46	start off, make up.
19	point out, get by.	47	read out, hang up.
20	go on, tear apart.	48	do up, set off.
21	get up, switch on.	49	fall over, slow down.
22	tuck in, turn off.	50	tidy up, carry on.
23	look out for, get on with.	51	do with, wear out.
24	show to, take care of.	52	hand in, tear up.
25	light up, send for.	53	strike as, get through.
26	get down to, keep up.	54	stand for, knock out.
27	look round, check in.	55	break through, get round to.
28	take off, wash up.	56	get over, knock down.

57	break down, get off.		79	put off, run into.
58	believe in, put off.		80	go off, turn into.
59	hold on, be over.		81	show round, look over.
60	make of, tell from.		82	give up, settle down.
61	long for, take over.		83	tire out, catch up.
62	wind up, switch off.		84	think of, lie behind.
63	be all for, think over.		85	know of, turn to.
64	carry out, draw up.		86	be off, turn up.
65	ask for, put up.		87	bring up, live up to.
66	hear of, stand for.		88	look forward to, come out.
67	speak out, break off.		89	line up, call out.
68	take up, get hold of.		90	leave out, join in.
69	turn over, look through.		91	give back, get through.
70	hand over, end up.		92	put back, see off.
71	hurry up, put out.		93	get in touch with, go on.
72	keep on, put up.		94	send away for, go up.
73	put up with, throw out.		95	move in, make up for.
74	get on, hold up.		96	speed up, turn on.
75	come across, look up.		97	look into, see to.
76	make out, call off.		98	turn back, be in.
77	do with, get down to.		99	pick out, save up.
78	come about, speak for.		100	tell off, take down.

Index

Answer Key

Suggested answers only are given for all the Exercise B questions, since more than one answer is usually possible.

UNIT 1
Exercise A
1 Do (it) up
2 took off
3 get up
4 showed (him) to
5 Put out
6 speed up
7 put (them) out
8 do up

Exercise B
1 You put it out.
2 You do them up.
3 You put them out.
4 A plane or helicopter takes off.
5 I get up at eight o'clock.
6 Yes, you can do it up.
7 When you press the accelerator.
8 She shows you to your seat.

UNIT 2
Exercise A
1 do (your buttons) up
2 wake (him) up
3 made up
4 get up/wake up
5 wake up
6 kept on
7 see to
8 made (her eyes) up

Exercise B
1 I wake up at half past seven.
2 You can do up a shirt, shoes, a zip or buttons.
3 You cook it and serve it.
4 No, I will only keep on studying it until I speak very well.
5 Yes, I get up straight away.
6 He makes up.
7 Yes, she keeps on asking difficult questions.
8 A personnel manager sees to staff problems.

UNIT 3
Exercise A
1 sorted out
2 sort out/see to
3 think (much) of
4 was off
5 make (anything) of
6 shown to
7 is off
8 sort (them) out

Exercise B
1 I think it is interesting.
2 When a visitor is just going to leave.
3 By arranging them according to author, title or subject.
4 I would try to get a refund.
5 I find it quite difficult to understand.
6 An engineer sees to it.
7 I think it is getting better.
8 You could arrange them in numerical order in each suit.

UNIT 4
Exercise A
1 sort out
2 hold on
3 look after
4 sort (it) out
5 took off
6 look after
7 check in
8 called out

Exercise B
1 He helps people sort out their marriage problems.
2 You can see planes landing and taking off.
3 It is for calling out announcements.
4 You must check in.
5 The Minister of Finance has to try to sort them out.
6 A babysitter looks after children.
7 When she wanted you to wait.
8 A zoo keeper looks after them.

UNIT 5
Exercise A
1 speed up
2 thinking of
3 run out of
4 make out
5 giving up
6 thought of
7 give up
8 go on

Exercise B
1 You press harder on the accelerator.
2 No, I've never thought of it.
3 I would have to give up.
4 When it had run out.
5 He must not go on until he has given details of his address and insurance to the other driver or the police.
6 In a city you can make out distant buildings.
7 I'm not sure, but perhaps Jules Verne first thought of it.
8 She would go on.

UNIT 6
Exercise A
1 slowed down
2 pick (the tickets) up
3 run out
4 is in
5 tire (me) out
6 pick (you) up
7 run out of
8 made (herself) up

Exercise B
1 When you know he will be in.
2 Running for a bus, shopping on Saturdays, and carrying heavy luggage.
3 Yes, I have.
4 It slows down when it is going uphill.
5 I would feel completely tired out.
6 Actors, models and television presenters are made up.
7 You could pick up a parcel sent by rail.
8 Yes, I try to slow down and relax.

UNIT 7

Exercise A
1 work out
2 faced up to/woke up to
3 keep (them) up
4 wake up to
5 work (it) out
6 cope with
7 go on
8 keep up

Exercise B
1 They will be able to go on if there is a substitute for petrol.
2 Some people can.
3 I could not cope with a lorry hitting my house.
4 Sometimes you can work it out from the context.
5 It realises something must be done to increase sales and tries to take action.
6 You should use a foam-based fire-extinguisher.
7 No, they often wake up to them too late.
8 I've only kept up the subjects that have been useful to me.

UNIT 8

Exercise A
1 put (it) out
2 come across
3 make (it) out
4 carried out
5 cleared (that) up
6 carried out
7 got down to
8 clear up

Exercise B
1 They must carry out tests when they cannot diagnose the problem immediately.
2 When it is an electrical fire.
3 They very seldom come across it.
4 You can clear up an untidy room, a confusing situation, or an overgrown garden.
5 They try to carry them out.
6 It is difficult when you have just had a good lunch.
7 It depends. Sometimes it is difficult.
8 I occasionally come across people I knew when I was a child.

UNIT 9

Exercise A
1 look round
2 tired (him) out
3 pick up
4 know of
5 look round
6 see (our friends) off
7 picked (it) up
8 gets down to

Exercise B
1 I know of one or two in Edinburgh.
2 You could pick up a lot if you spoke to people.
3 You would see someone off at a station or airport.
4 Rowing and long-distance running would tire me out.
5 By watching the team in a few matches.
6 I get down to work about half past nine.
7 When you were thinking of buying it.
8 You would see your guests off at the door.

UNIT 10

Exercise A
1 look after
2 is off
3 carried out
4 picked up
5 is off
6 holding on
7 keep up
8 hold on

Exercise B
1 It might have been the 1987 Knightsbridge deposit box robbery (£30,000,000).
2 You can keep it up by reading a little regularly.
3 If you had to get some information from them.
4 She looks after patients in hospital.
5 If I had to tell people that the party was off for some reason.
6 I have kept up a few friendships.
7 You would pick up some idea of the value of things.
8 You should carry out basic safety checks every week.

UNIT 11

Exercise A
1 wait for
2 get rid of
3 made (it) up
4 came across
5 waiting for
6 keep on
7 get rid of
8 put up with

Exercise B
1 You can't get rid of it completely, but taking aspirin may help you feel better.
2 They wait for a bus.
3 You have to put up with taxes and rising prices.
4 It is when you make up a story that isn't true.
5 You usually come across them outside cities.
6 Nothing. You have to put up with it.
7 Keep on trying.
8 Some of them may be partly true but most are made up.

UNIT 12

Exercise A
1 ring up
2 heard of
3 make of
4 going on
5 gave up
6 ring (him) up
7 strike (you) as
8 gave up

Exercise B
1 By ringing her up.
2 The Olympic Games are held.
3 Yes, I have heard of him.
4 I think they show a lot of imagination.
5 It is raining and people are getting wet.
6 You should give it up to someone who needs it more than you.
7 It strikes me as odd that there is no cure for the common cold.
8 I have heard of Hokusai and Utamaro.

Answer Key

UNIT 13

Exercise A
1 do without
2 face up to
3 look into
4 work (it) out
5 go ahead
6 work out
7 is all for
8 going ahead

Exercise B
1 Many people think we could do without them.
2 I'm all for higher salaries and lower taxes.
3 You can do it by working out the answer.
4 You would go ahead and do it.
5 When there is an unpleasant situation and you know you must do something about it.
6 I could do without fuel bills, noisy neighbours and my car not working.
7 They look into suspected crimes.
8 Yes, I'm all for it.

UNIT 14

Exercise A
1 lived up to
2 see (him) off
3 cut off from
4 get hold of
5 put (you) up
6 cuts (the island) off from
7 live up to
8 look round

Exercise B
1 They go to see people off.
2 Occasionally I put a friend up for the night.
3 It is cut off from the rest of the world.
4 You would look round.
5 By asking him or a friend of his.
6 If they win they live up to them.
7 You would see her off at the airport.
8 You can get hold of cheap fresh food and household articles.

UNIT 15

Exercise A
1 went through
2 worn out
3 cleared up
4 got on
5 worn out
6 slowed down
7 deal with
8 slow down

Exercise B
1 You get on a bus at the bus-stop.
2 You feel worn out.
3 After the rain has stopped it clears up.
4 They deal with passport applications.
5 They go through them to check the answers.
6 He slows down.
7 I wouldn't. I would get someone else to deal with it.
8 He goes through it to correct the mistakes.

UNIT 16

Exercise A
1 cope with
2 find out
3 get rid of
4 send away for
5 cope with
6 spoke out
7 lie behind
8 find (that) out

Exercise B
1 You could send away for a set of saucepans or a sweater or information about a pension.
2 To find out the times of trains.
3 Governments usually act according to a political theory.
4 I would turn off the mains tap.
5 I would speak out if I was really indignant about something.
6 You could try asking an English person.
7 By going to a dentist.
8 By sending away for it.

UNIT 17

Exercise A
1 drop in
2 hurry up
3 pick up
4 heard of
5 looking for
6 set off
7 looking for
8 drop in

Exercise B
1 You set off.
2 When I wanted to see him at his home or office.
3 I would hurry up.
4 I have heard of most of the big ones.
5 I would look for a reconstruction of one in a museum.
6 Friends often drop in at my house.
7 It stops to pick up passengers.
8 I would start looking for them.

UNIT 18

Exercise A
1 ran over
2 do with
3 carried on
4 waited for
5 do with
6 Turn (the lights) off
7 carry on
8 go ahead

Exercise B
1 It could do with a good clean.
2 I turn it off.
3 You might get run over by a lorry.
4 When I knew it was all right to do it I would go ahead.
5 Sometimes you have to wait for hours.
6 I could do with a holiday, a new car, more free time and a decent typewriter.
7 I turn off the light.
8 They will probably carry on until the petrol has run out.

UNIT 19
Exercise A
1 lies behind/lay behind
2 broke off
3 pointed out
4 mistaken (it) for
5 pointed (it) out
6 hung up
7 mistook (your umbrella) for
8 struck (me) as

Exercise B
1 You would hang up at the end of a phone call.
2 No, it doesn't strike me as odd at all.
3 I can't imagine what lies behind it.
4 He points out interesting details of tourist attractions.
5 Yes, somebody once mistook me for my brother.
6 You would break off if you had to go.
7 I don't think I would mistake one for the other.
8 No, we usually say goodbye and hang up at the same time.

UNIT 20
Exercise A
1 send away for
2 going on
3 living up to
4 know of
5 going on
6 looking for
7 put (you) up
8 know of

Exercise B
1 Often hotels do not live up to their descriptions in the brochures.
2 There are lots of artistic events.
3 Yes, lots of places have colder winters.
4 I would go to an estate agent.
5 When you wanted somewhere to stay.
6 You can find out by listening to the news.
7 It is a way of buying things by sending away for them.
8 He would probably be looking for alcohol or tobacco or drugs.

UNIT 21
Exercise A
1 build up
2 go up
3 get by
4 Ask (the examiner) for
5 built up
6 put up with
7 get by on
8 asking for

Exercise B
1 Yes, I can put up with quite a lot.
2 It helps them build up their strength.
3 Yes, I'm all for that idea.
4 I can get by on my salary.
5 It goes up about once a year or so.
6 He asks for money from other people.
7 It goes up.
8 When you wanted to ask for something.

UNIT 22
Exercise A
1 turned down
2 took over
3 look into
4 come up
5 went through
6 took over
7 fit in with
8 turn (it) down

Exercise B
1 When it did not fit in with my own plans.
2 He takes over.
3 Not very often.
4 You might go through a newspaper if you were looking for a job.
5 A private detective would look into a personal matter.
6 You would turn it down if you did not want to go out.
7 A teacher goes through students' homework.
8 Sometimes I arrange that my holidays fit in with those of a friend.

UNIT 23
Exercise A
1 decided on
2 turned up
3 do without
4 poured in
5 cut off from
6 pouring into
7 tore (the family) apart
8 do without

Exercise B
1 You cannot do without air, warmth and water.
2 Yes, to be an island it must be cut off from the mainland.
3 Sometimes I turn up late for work.
4 I would decide on one of them.
5 They pour in on the first day of the sales.
6 A heavy storm could tear a ship apart.
7 Earthquakes could tear a country apart.
8 He must feel rather cut off from the rest of the world.

UNIT 24
Exercise A
1 stand for
2 put (us) back
3 made up
4 looked through
5 speak for
6 broke off
7 made (it) up
8 stand for

Exercise B
1 No, usually I just look through it.
2 She speaks for a group of people.
3 When official summer time ends and days get shorter.
4 People pushing in front of me in a queue and being given the wrong change.
5 No, sometimes they adapt existing stories.
6 Yes, in case there is something important.
7 If there was tension between the two countries.
8 Usually the Foreign Affairs Minister speaks for the country.

Answer Key

UNIT 25
Exercise A
1 find out
2 cut off
3 moved in
4 call (you) back
5 get through
6 ring (him) up
7 cut (it) off
8 call back

Exercise B
1 Copernicus found out before Galileo did.
2 They would do it if the water was contaminated.
3 She would move in.
4 I would call back later.
5 It is for ringing people up.
6 You use it to find out things.
7 You would not be able to get through if you tried to ring him up.
8 Gas, electricity, water.

UNIT 26
Exercise A
1 made up for
2 get over
3 turned out
4 set off
5 give up
6 worn (them) out
7 make up for
8 turned out

Exercise B
1 No, it is not easy to give it up.
2 Excessive or incorrect use can wear a machine out.
3 You might get over it quickly if it was a small shock.
4 A ship sets off from a port.
5 No, sometimes they turn out worse than expected.
6 If I could, I would try to make up for it.
7 I could not give up drinking coffee or driving.
8 They use physiotherapy to help patients get over rheumatism.

UNIT 27
Exercise A
1 Take care of
2 do with
3 washed (the glasses) up
4 tidy (your room) up
5 threw (it) away
6 got hold of
7 wash up
8 tidy up

Exercise B
1 You wash up after a meal.
2 You tidy up after a party.
3 No, you cannot throw a car away.
4 Zoo keepers take care of animals in a zoo.
5 A tired and busy person could do with a rest.
6 I usually throw it away.
7 I would hire or borrow one.
8 A bodyguard takes care of someone important.

UNIT 28
Exercise A
1 turned to
2 get away with
3 taken away
4 spoke out
5 tore (the city) apart
6 turn to
7 longed for
8 longing for

Exercise B
1 He gets away with the crime.
2 Morphine takes away pain.
3 Yes, most of the time I long for a holiday.
4 I would turn to my bank manager.
5 A tornado could tear a place apart.
6 If I knew I would be on my own I probably would not speak out.
7 I got away with doing the minimum amount of work at school.
8 I buy take-away food about once a week.

UNIT 29
Exercise A
1 tell (Jane) from
2 picked out
3 drop in
4 look out for
5 stocked up with
6 tell (a painting by Rubens) from
7 picked out
8 stock up with

Exercise B
1 Yes, I did once, when I was leaving a party.
2 They stock up with petrol.
3 An African elephant has bigger ears.
4 They pick out the books they want to borrow.
5 You would look out for cars coming towards you.
6 You would drop in to buy some flowers.
7 By tasting it, if you know about wine, or by looking at the label.
8 They look out for bargains.

UNIT 30
Exercise A
1 carried on
2 asked (the boss) for
3 pointed out
4 thrown (it) away
5 Call back
6 threw away
7 turned down
8 pointed out

Exercise B
1 I would turn it down if I had a better offer.
2 You would call back to see the results.
3 Because the opportunity might not come again.
4 A museum guide points out important exhibits.
5 You would ask for a table first and the bill last.
6 No, if the doctor told me to stop I would not carry on.
7 You could turn down an invitation or an offer.
8 A ticket inspector asks you for your ticket.

UNIT 31

Exercise A
1 get on with
2 poured in
3 make up for
4 looking forward to
5 breakthrough
6 get on with
7 draw (it) up
8 break through

Exercise B
1 Yes, I look forward to going out on Friday nights.
2 He draws up plans for buildings.
3 You would get on with what you were doing.
4 Finding some money could make up for losing your wallet.
5 Water pours in.
6 I'm looking forward to spending Christmas with my family.
7 It breaks through the sound barrier at the speed of sound (1220 km per hour).
8 It might have to increase taxes.

UNIT 32

Exercise A
1 come out
2 fit in with
3 join in
4 drop out of
5 grow up
6 longed for
7 comes out
8 fit in with

Exercise B
1 Yes, it would help if we could all speak one common language.
2 Two editions have come out so far.
3 You could join in a game or a discussion.
4 They grow up.
5 Because of illness, lack of interest or the need to get a job.
6 Arabic does not have a Latin base.
7 I grew up in Madrid.
8 Spectators could join in a game of football on the beach.

UNIT 33

Exercise A
1 put back
2 catch up with
3 knocked down
4 pull (himself) together
5 went through
6 catch up with
7 build (your strength) up
8 went through

Exercise B
1 No, but my brother was knocked down by a cyclist.
2 A delay would hold you up.
3 You could build up your strength, or your financial reserves; a country could build up its army.
4 You would have to try to catch up.
5 If I was unable to control myself.
6 No, at the first sign of toothache I would go to the dentist.
7 They do it to build up their health and fitness.
8 They try to pull themselves together.

UNIT 34

Exercise A
1 wrap (their parcels) up
2 ended up
3 tore (it) up
4 take over
5 let (him) out
6 ended up
7 tell (one) from
8 let (it) out

Exercise B
1 They wrap it up for you.
2 They are let out when classes finish.
3 It's possible. It is quite difficult to tell one kind of whisky from another.
4 The vice-president takes over.
5 I would tear it up when I had finished reading it.
6 You could end up in prison.
7 You would wrap up well.
8 Unwanted notes or an abusive letter.

UNIT 35

Exercise A
1 brought up
2 came up with
3 go on about
4 left (anything) out
5 get by
6 went on about
7 come up with
8 look through

Exercise B
1 I could go on about modern art or what is wrong with my car.
2 People bring up various points.
3 No, some problems are probably insoluble.
4 My teacher looks through my answers.
5 At present no country can get by without oil.
6 No, I normally remember everything important.
7 I occasionally look through one.
8 Spain, Portugal, Holland, Italy, Eire.

UNIT 36

Exercise A
1 put (it) off/call (it) off
2 ran into
3 turned out
4 come up
5 call (their holiday) off/put (their holiday) off
6 count (him) out
7 come up
8 count (me) out

Exercise B
1 He would have to put the meeting off.
2 Problems of grammar and vocabulary often come up.
3 They might run into training problems.
4 No, they turned out much better.
5 It would be called off.
6 He would have to count the player out.
7 It would be put off.
8 You would have to call it off.

Answer Key

UNIT 37

Exercise A
1 turns up
2 think about
3 started off
4 settled down
5 speak for
6 was over
7 started off
8 turned up

Exercise B
1 Yes, it is possible to speak for yourself.
2 When the meal was over.
3 I would try.
4 I would think about it.
5 Yes. In fact, most towns start off as villages.
6 You would settle down.
7 I will go home.
8 I often think about what I have to do the next day.

UNIT 38

Exercise A
1 Switch (the light) on
2 move in
3 broke in/had broken in
4 sent for
5 cut (you) off
6 look in
7 break in
8 send for

Exercise B
1 By sending for it.
2 A lamp, a record-player, a heater, a fire-alarm.
3 Yes, occasionally people look in.
4 I moved in last year.
5 The phone would be cut off.
6 They break into people's houses.
7 I would look in at the hospital to see how he was.
8 Fortunately my home has never been broken into.

UNIT 39

Exercise A
1 pick out
2 read out
3 opened up
4 turned (the page) over
5 take care of
6 lit up
7 turn (them) over
8 lit up

Exercise B
1 I would take care of it.
2 My face would light up.
3 I will turn over.
4 He sailed round the southern tip of Africa and opened up the sea trading route.
5 You would read out a public announcement.
6 When they want a witness to pick out a suspect.
7 Some butchers let you pick out the meat you want.
8 Somebody reads out the notes taken at the previous meeting.

UNIT 40

Exercise A
1 turned to
2 called (it) off
3 give up
4 broke through
5 stocked up with
6 stand for
7 give up
8 stand for

Exercise B
1 I would have to give it up.
2 You would turn to a solicitor or a lawyer.
3 The discovery of penicillin is perhaps the most important breakthrough so far.
4 You would stock up with fresh fruit and vegetables.
5 People not paying taxes, too high inflation, excessive levels of corruption.
6 The race would be called off.
7 Sometimes people turn to me if they think I can help them.
8 A few athletes have broken through this barrier.

UNIT 41

Exercise A
1 called on
2 are after
3 handed over
4 Look out for
5 go off
6 get away with
7 Hand (it) over
8 went off

Exercise B
1 You might look out for uncommon animals or plants.
2 The police don't let them get away with it.
3 It goes off.
4 Sometimes I am called on to speak at a meeting.
5 Probably a few people do get away with it.
6 The police cars would be driving fast and using their lights and sirens.
7 They call on them to resign.
8 You would look out for a bargain.

UNIT 42

Exercise A
1 think (it) over
2 end up
3 put/puts (her) off
4 count on
5 believe in
6 went through
7 ended up
8 believed in

Exercise B
1 I would want some time to think it over.
2 Yes, a lot of people believe in God.
3 In most countries you can count on good weather in summer.
4 If I really wanted to work in a theatre nothing would put me off.
5 Yes, you go through a lot of pain if you burn yourself.
6 It ended up with America becoming independent.
7 No, because my car is quite old.
8 I would think it over carefully.

70

UNIT 43

Exercise A
1 put (it) away
2 tell (children) off
3 dry up
4 tidy (the garden) up
5 settle down
6 tucked in
7 put (the Christmas decorations) away
8 settle down

Exercise B
1 You would do it when a child was behaving badly.
2 They like to be tucked in.
3 You dry up.
4 It settles down.
5 I would tidy the room up.
6 A food-mixer, a hairdryer.
7 Yes, once when I tried to park in the wrong place.
8 You would collect all the plates and glasses, wash up and clean the floor.

UNIT 44

Exercise A
1 try (that coat) on
2 fall over
3 knocked (him) out
4 drew (the soldiers) up
5 get on with
6 held (the trains) up
7 fell over
8 drawn up

Exercise B
1 He falls over.
2 You might be knocked out.
3 They try on clothes.
4 Things get held up.
5 A tie, a pair of socks.
6 On big occasions outside the royal or presidential palace.
7 People get on with their work.
8 The trains are held up.

UNIT 45

Exercise A
1 tore (the letter) up
2 fill in
3 write (your telephone number) down
4 came out
5 looked (it) up
6 stand for
7 tore (it) up
8 look up/write down

Exercise B
1 You fill it in.
2 They stand for your full name.
3 They come out every day.
4 Yes, sometimes I write them down.
5 No, I have not torn one up so far.
6 You could look it up in an encyclopedia.
7 You could try writing it down.
8 You have to fill in an immigration form.

UNIT 46

Exercise A
1 saving up
2 take up
3 Bringing up
4 started off
5 go with
6 give (it) back
7 started off
8 save up

Exercise B
1 *Down* goes with *up*.
2 You have to give them back within the time period you are allowed to keep them for.
3 You would save up for a holiday, or a new car.
4 They bring up their children.
5 I would like to take up water-skiing.
6 You would start off by getting some lessons on a dry slope.
7 You would give it back.
8 Because I wanted to be able to speak it.

UNIT 47

Exercise A
1 looked (it) over
2 switched (the light) off
3 broken in
4 looked over
5 show (you) round
6 took down
7 break into
8 look over

Exercise B
1 A guide shows people round.
2 They take down notes.
3 You switch off the light.
4 You would think it over.
5 They look over it carefully.
6 The door or a window would be broken.
7 They take down notes.
8 You would switch it off.

UNIT 48

Exercise A
1 lined up
2 put up
3 got off
4 open up
5 turn back
6 hand over
7 lined up
8 turn back

Exercise B
1 He would put his hands up.
2 You would turn back.
3 He opens up his shop.
4 You get off the train.
5 When they were waiting for the first day of a big sale.
6 He would have to hand over everything in his pockets.
7 When they know the answer to a question.
8 A horse, a motorbike, a train, an escalator.

Answer Key

UNIT 49

Exercise A
1 got through
2 stay up
3 think about
4 put (the match) off
5 wrote out
6 hand (the form) in
7 stayed up
8 write (them) out

Exercise B
1 You would stay up.
2 Each exercise takes about five minutes to get through.
3 You might write out the ones you found difficult to remember.
4 You hand in your answers.
5 You would have to put off the dinner.
6 Sometimes it is sensible to think about what you are going to say.
7 You have to hand in your passport every ten years in the United Kingdom.
8 It will take a few lessons to get through.

UNIT 50

Exercise A
1 come up with
2 count on
3 believe in
4 called on
5 went off
6 put up
7 counting on
8 called on

Exercise B
1 They put it up last year.
2 They keep coming up with new ideas all the time.
3 Yes, a lot of children believe in Father Christmas.
4 No, I have never seen one go off.
5 They call on them to surrender.
6 Usually you can count on it.
7 An atheist is someone who does not believe in God.
8 They put up the price of petrol for motorists.

UNIT 51

Exercise A
1 count (him) out
2 take off
3 drop out
4 is on
5 turned into
6 join in
7 is (the fire) on
8 join in

Exercise B
1 Yes, it is on at the moment.
2 It turns into steam.
3 You take off your wet clothes.
4 He is counted out.
5 He would probably have to drop out of the course.
6 Because a lot of countries were in alliance with each other.
7 You take off your jacket or your sweater.
8 It turns into alcohol.

UNIT 52

Exercise A
1 catch (you) up
2 wind (it) up
3 run into
4 breaking down
5 get in touch with
6 held up
7 catch up
8 wind (them) up

Exercise B
1 You have to wind it up unless it is electric.
2 No, I got here on time.
3 You could phone her or write to her.
4 It breaks down.
5 He would try to catch up.
6 You would try not to let it hold you up for too long.
7 By overheating, losing petrol, developing an electrical fault, or getting a flat battery.
8 The traffic is held up.

UNIT 53

Exercise A
1 sent (it) off
2 told (the dog) off
3 come about
4 left out
5 looking forward to
6 get on with
7 sent off
8 came about

Exercise B
1 You could try telling him off.
2 I had an American pen-friend and wanted to write to her in English.
3 They wouldn't be my friends if I didn't get on with them.
4 Scotland has been left out.
5 My holidays and Christmas.
6 You send them off.
7 No, I have answered them all.
8 The British are as easy to get on with as any nationality.

UNIT 54

Exercise A
1 pull (yourself) together
2 taken (it) up
3 fall through
4 threw (him) out
5 am after
6 get round to
7 throw (him) out
8 get round to

Exercise B
1 They get thrown out.
2 People who are after antiques.
3 You would probably try to pull yourself together and do better.
4 I took it up three years ago.
5 No, he doesn't get round to them immediately.
6 You would try to arrange another holiday.
7 I would make sure I kept it myself.
8 No, I have never thought of taking it up as a career.

UNIT 55

Exercise A
1 put forward
2 lit up
3 Turn (the television) on
4 get on with
5 came about
6 ring (you) back
7 put (it) forward
8 come about

Exercise B
1 I turn on the radio.
2 They light up the actors on the stage.
3 I get on very well with my sister.
4 If we had been cut off I would ring back.
5 Isaac Newton.
6 One theory is that it broke off from the sun.
7 A motor, a radio, a cooker, a tap.
8 The lamp lights up.

UNIT 56

Exercise A
1 look in
2 took off
3 wrap up
4 try on
5 go with
6 throw (them) out
7 took (it) off
8 throw out

Exercise B
1 A present, a parcel.
2 Grey goes well with yellow.
3 You would throw it out.
4 No, you would not try on a shirt.
5 I would take them off.
6 Yes, sometimes I look in at the supermarket.
7 Chicken and rice.
8 You could try an old castle, or a theatrical costume supplier's.

UNIT 57

Exercise A
1 broke down
2 get over
3 deal with
4 Send for
5 puts (a lot of people) off
6 turn into
7 dealing with
8 puts (me) off

Exercise B
1 They can make things turn into other things.
2 By phoning and asking for one to come.
3 Yes, it puts me off.
4 They break down.
5 It turns into mud.
6 It takes about three months to get over a broken arm.
7 The police deal with traffic jams.
8 You would send for an ambulance.

UNIT 58

Exercise A
1 handed (your work) in
2 wrote down
3 turned (the parcel) over
4 read out
5 get through
6 put (it) forward
7 read out
8 write (it) down

Exercise B
1 I will get through it very soon.
2 You hand it in.
3 They put forward their views on Government policy.
4 You turn over.
5 Someone reads out the results.
6 To write down people's names and addresses.
7 I get through more work in the afternoons.
8 You turn it over.

UNIT 59

Exercise A
1 took (the prisoner) away
2 saving up
3 falls through
4 get round to
5 look over
6 show (you) round
7 get round to
8 fallen through

Exercise B
1 No, I would have to save up for a new car.
2 I would show him round.
3 He takes the plates away.
4 I might get round to reading it again next year.
5 You would look it over carefully.
6 I might have to give up the idea.
7 It would take me about five years or more, depending on the type of yacht.
8 No, you can take them away.

UNIT 60

Exercise A
1 sent (them) off
2 took down
3 write (the report) out
4 look up
5 put (our books) away
6 get in touch with
7 wrote out
8 taken down

Exercise B
1 He takes down notes on the proceedings.
2 They send a lot of parcels and letters off before Christmas.
3 A cheque, a report, a piece of music.
4 By looking it up in a dictionary.
5 You put them away.
6 By satellite.
7 It is for looking up people's phone numbers.
8 No, you would not put it away.